Workbook

EXPLORING French

THIRD EDITION

Joan G. Sheeran

EMC Publishing

ST. PAUL • LOS ANGELES

Editorial Director: Alejandro Vargas
Editor: Diana Moen
Production Editor: Amy McGuire

Production Specialist: Parkwood Composition
Cover Designer: Leslie Anderson
Proofreader: Jamie Bryant, B-books, Ltd.

ISBN 978-0-82193-481-4

© 2008 by EMC Publishing, a division of EMC Corporation
875 Montreal Way
St. Paul, MN 55102
E-mail: educate@emcp.com
Web site: www.emcp.com

16 15   8 9 10

Nom: _____ Date: _____

Unit 1

A **Comment s'appellent-ils?** *(Can you identify each of the following French names?)*

1. a girl's version of the name Georges _____

2. a boy's version of the name Michelle _____

3. a boy's name starting with an F _____

4. a girl's name starting with an N _____

5. a girl's name starting with an A _____

6. a boy's name starting with an A _____

7. a boy's name starting with an H _____

8. a girl's name starting with a C _____

9. a boy's name starting with a T _____

10. a girl's name starting with a J _____

B In the list below are some French names of girls and boys. Make two separate lists, one for the *jeunes filles* (girls) and the other for the *garçons* (boys).

Jean-François Manon **Laure** **Didier** *Emmanuelle* Olivier
Isabelle Gilles Chantal **Guillaume** **Michel** Sophie

Noms de jeunes filles   **Noms de garçons**

_____   _____

_____   _____

_____   _____

_____   _____

_____   _____

C Match the situation on the left with the appropriate response on the right.

A: Situation

1. _____ You say goodbye to a friend.

2. _____ You ask a new student what his name is.

3. _____ You say "Hi" to a girl.

4. _____ You make a mistake and you feel bad about it.

5. _____ You wish a friend well on her English test.

6. _____ You say good night to your parents.

B: Response

A. Bonne chance.

B. Je regrette.

C. Comment t'appelles-tu?

D. Au revoir, René.

E. Bonne nuit.

F. Salut, Chloé.

D Complete the following dialogues.

> **Modèle:**   CHARLES: Bonjour, Monsieur Gide.
> MONSIEUR GIDE: Bonjour, <u>Charles</u>.

1. PHILIPPE: Salut, Chantal.

   CHANTAL: Salut, _____.

2. Comment t'appelles-tu?

   _____ m'appelle Yvette.

3. Enchantée, Michel.

   Avec _____, Marie-Alix.

4. Chantal, tu parles arabe, n'est-ce pas?

   _____, je ne parle pas arabe.

5. Midori, tu parles japonais?

   _____, je parle japonais.

6. Parles-tu allemand, Anja?

   Oui, je parle _____.

7. Comment vas-tu, Michelle?

   Bien, _____. Et toi?

8. Au revoir, Théo.

   _____ demain, Léa.

9. Merci, Mme Bizet.

   _____, Philippe.

10. Comment s'appelle le garçon?

    Il _____ Bernard.

E Look closely at the French names of different countries on the left. Since most of these words look similar to the English versions, you should have little difficulty understanding them. In Column 1 write the English name of the country and in Column 2, the French name of the language spoken there.

le pays (country)	nom du pays (English name of country)	la langue (French name of language)
1. la France	_____	_____
2. l'Italie	_____	_____
3. la Chine	_____	_____
4. l'Égypte	_____	_____
5. l'Allemagne	_____	_____
6. l'Angleterre	_____	_____
7. l'Espagne	_____	_____
8. le Japon	_____	_____
9. la Russie	_____	_____

F Give the following girl and boy French names. Then complete the dialogue.

(Boy's name) _____: Salut! Comment t'appelles- _____?

(Girl's name) _____: Je m'appelle _____. Et toi?

(Boy's name) _____: Je m'appelle _____.

(Girl's name) _____: _____.

(Boy's name) _____: Avec _____.

G *Parlons!* **Imagine that it's the first day of school. You and your partner play the roles of two students who haven't met yet. In the course of your conversation:**

1. . . . say "hello" or "hi" to your classmate.

2. . . . ask your classmate what his or her name is.

3. . . . ask your classmate how he or she is.

4. . . . tell your classmate "Good luck!"

5. . . . tell your classmate "Good-bye" or "See you later."

H *Les mots cachés.* **Find and circle the French version of the words and expressions found on the right. Remember they may go forward, backward, up, down, or diagonally.**

S	E	M	M	A	N	U	E	L	L	E	J	S	U	I	N
G	W	J	I	A	M	Q	C	C	D	W	M	G	O	C	N
L	J	G	W	U	G	Y	S	A	L	U	T	H	Q	W	D
O	M	O	F	R	S	M	Z	B	J	V	D	I	O	R	I
Y	U	Q	I	E	R	E	T	W	Z	O	Z	E	I	X	J
D	N	I	P	V	Y	K	Z	S	P	Z	T	K	P	Z	T
O	R	U	W	O	U	D	L	M	D	T	C	T	N	O	Y
B	T	T	T	I	N	Y	R	R	E	H	I	C	R	E	M
O	T	M	P	R	L	E	N	R	B	C	S	G	O	W	H
N	X	A	U	R	V	O	G	Z	O	G	B	I	P	K	M
N	V	R	J	J	D	E	D	X	N	K	L	L	B	K	L
E	E	H	Z	R	R	L	L	C	J	W	E	L	P	X	X
N	E	V	A	E	Z	N	Q	X	O	T	O	E	R	S	O
U	L	P	J	L	F	U	H	A	U	V	H	S	E	C	I
I	Q	Z	U	O	N	O	Y	T	R	L	Z	Y	J	M	Q
T	Q	P	Q	K	M	X	D	A	U	M	P	T	M	P	X

1. Excuse me

2. boy's name starting with a "G"

3. Good night

4. Yes

5. I'm sorry

6. girl's name starting with an "E"

7. Hi

8. Good-bye

9. Hello

10. Thank you

I **Look at the clippings of realia to find the requested information or answer the questions.**

...ça te va?

Immigration-Québec

Des gens à votre service!

Bienvenue dans le Vieux-Montréal,
pôle historique de réputation mondiale !

Je vous souhaite un agréable séjour parmi nous.

BENOIT LABONTÉ
Maire de l'arrondissement,
et Membre du comité exécutif,
responsable de la Culture,
du Patrimoine et du Centre-ville

Ville-Marie
Montréal

Pour vous conseiller et répondre à toutes vos questions, le ministère de l'Immigration et des Communautés culturelles (MICC) met à votre disposition les services Immigration-Québec dans les principales villes du Québec.

**BIENVENUE
AU CLUB**

Sincères remerciements

1. Find the name of a city.

   _____

2. Find the name of the province in which this city is located.

   _____

3. What is the country?

   _____

4. Which word says "Welcome"?

   _____

5. The mayor of the old-city district is pictured here. What is his first name?

   _____

6. What does the word *je* mean in English?

   _____

7. Find and write down the words that say: "I wish you a pleasant stay with us."

   _____

8. Find an expression that asks how you are.

   _____

9. Find an expression that means you are grateful.

   _____

10. Find the three words that show you are ready to help others.

   _____

Unit 2

A How is each object used? Match the French expression on the left with its English function on the right.

1. _____ un livre

2. _____ une fenêtre

3. _____ une peinture

4. _____ une corbeille à papier

5. _____ une carte

A. lets in fresh air and daylight

B. place to put waste paper

C. makes a plain room look more attractive

D. opens up new worlds of adventure, fantasy, travel, and information

E. shows you geographical locations

B Identify each of the following classroom objects, beginning with the appropriate article. (*En français, s'il te plaît.*)

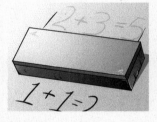

1. C'est _____.

2. C'est _____.

3. C'est _____.

4.   C'est _____.

5.   C'est _____.

6.   C'est _____.

7.   C'est _____.

8.   C'est _____.

9.   C'est _____.

10.   C'est _____.

C Name the classroom object most closely associated with each group of words. Begin with the article. *(En français, s'il te plaît.)*

Examples	Object
1. alarm digital cuckoo grandfather	_____
2. Sénégal Vietnam Norway Indonesia	_____
3. *The Adventures of Tom Sawyer* *Heidi* *Harry Potter* *The Wizard of Oz*	_____
4. loose-leaf lined unlined graph	_____
5. straight back armless office kitchen	_____

D List five items you might carry in your *sac à dos*. Remember to include the article.

1. _____

2. _____

3. _____

4. _____

5. _____

E Find your way through the *salle de classe*. Name the classroom objects you encounter on your way. Start at the entrance, or *Entrée*, and finish at the exit, or *Sortie*.

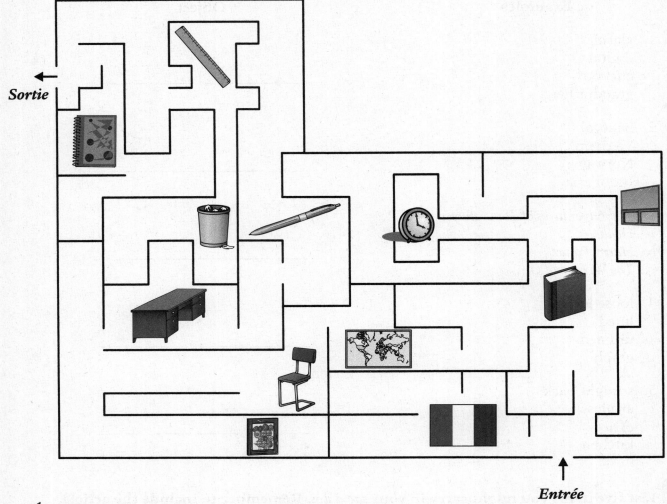

Sortie

Entrée

1. _____

2. _____

3. _____

4. _____

5. _____

F Your classmate tells you in French to do certain things. What does each command mean? Circle either A or B.

1. Écris en français.

   A. Write in French.   B. Say it in French.

2. Lis.

   A. Speak.   B. Read.

3. Lève la main.

   A. Raise your hand.   B. Go to the board.

4. Ferme le livre.

   A. Open the book.   B. Close the book.

5. Prends une feuille de papier.

   A. Take out a sheet of paper.   B. Turn on the computer.

6. Parle.

   A. Speak.   B. Listen.

G Find the word in the box that best completes each command. Then write it in the space provided.

> **français** tableau **livre** **ordinateur** ^main^ question ^image^

1. Lève la _____!

2. Parle _____!

3. Va au _____!

4. Réponds à la _____!

5. Allume l'_____!

6. Dessine une _____!

7. Ouvre le _____!

H Write a command suggested by the word cue on the left.

1. le crayon   _____

2. le livre   _____

3. la musique   _____

4. la fenêtre   _____

5. l'ordinateur _____

I Look at the clippings and answer the questions or provide the requested information.

1. What is the name of this room in French?

   _____

2. On the floor you see a backpack, or *sac à dos*. Make a list of what else you see in this room. *(En français, s'il te plaît.)*

   _____

   _____

3. What kind of book do you see on the right?

   _____

4. What word tells you that this book contains pictures?

   _____

5. What performs basic arithmetic problems? *(En français, s'il te plaît.)*

_____

6. This object works on both solar and battery power. Find the word for "solar."

_____

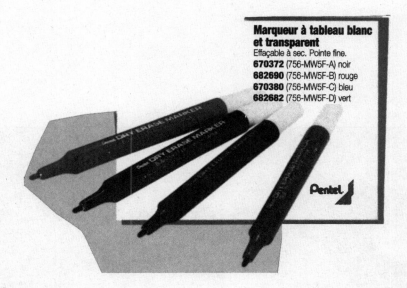

7. This ad shows another word for *feutre*. What is it?

_____

8. Find the phrase for "white board" (or "dry-erase board").

_____

TÉLÉCHARGE ► TRANSFÈRE ► ÉCOUTE
COMPREND: TROUSSE DE TÉLÉCHARGEMENT MP3*
• JUSQU'À 1 Go DE MÉMOIRE • CASQUE D'ÉCOUTE • CÂBLE USB

9. The clipping above has three commands: *Télécharge* (download), *Transfère* (transfer) and *Écoute*. What does this last command mean in English?

_____

10. Name the type of machine that provides the sounds for this listening device. *(En français, s'il te plaît.)*

_____

11. A *trousse* usually contains pencils or pens. However, in this clipping what does it hold?

_____

Unit 3

A **Circle the letter that tells you how many items are in each group.**

1.   A. seize   B. onze   C. neuf

2.   A. quinze   B. quatorze   C. trois

3.   A. huit   B. six   C. douze

4.   A. sept   B. onze   C. dix

5.   A. trente   B. treize   C. deux

6.   A. huit   B. quatre   C. vingt

B **Match the Arabic numerals on the left with the French words on the right.**

1. _____ 2   A. treize

2. _____ 8   B. trente-huit

3. _____ 13   C. quatre-vingt-douze

4. _____ 5   D. cinq

5. _____ 21   E. vingt et un

6. _____ 38   F. soixante-dix-sept

7. _____ 77   G. deux

8. _____ 11   H. onze

9. _____ 59   I. cinquante-neuf

10. _____ 92   J. huit

C **Find the sequencing pattern and then write the missing number in French.**

> sept   dix-neuf   cinquante   quatre-vingts   dix

1. quarante, _____, soixante

2. dix-huit, _____, vingt

3. six, _____, huit

4. cinq, _____, quinze

5. soixante-dix, _____, quatre-vingt-dix

D Combien de . . . ? Réponds aux questions en français. *(Answer the questions with a number written out in French.)*

1. How many planets are there in our solar system? _____

2. How many toes does the average person have? _____

3. How many feet does a duck have? _____

4. How many weeks comprise a year? _____

5. How many letters are there in the English alphabet? _____

6. How many items make up a dozen? _____

7. How many minutes are there in a half hour? _____

8. How many minutes are there in an hour? _____

9. How many days are there in January? _____

10. How many stomachs do you have? _____

E Express each sentence as a mathematical equation.

> **Modèle:** Dix divisé par deux font cinq.
> $\underline{10 \div 2 = 5}$

1. Trente moins vingt font dix.   _____

2. Deux cents et deux cents font quatre cents.   _____

3. Treize fois un font treize.   _____

4. Vingt divisé par quatre font cinq.   _____

F Solve the following French arithmetic problems. Write out each answer in French.

> **Modèle:** Combien font neuf moins un?
> <u>Neuf moins un font huit</u>.

1. Combien font trois fois quatre? _____

2. Combien font sept et quinze? _____

3. Combien font mille moins deux cents? _____

4. Combien font seize divisé par huit? _____

5. Combien font trente et quarante? _____

6. Combien font neuf moins cinq? _____

7. Combien font vingt-sept divisé par trois? _____

8. Combien font quatorze fois un? _____

9. Combien font douze et un? _____

10. Combien font quatre-vingt-neuf moins quatre? _____

G Il y a combien de . . . dans la salle de classe? *(How many things are there in your classroom? Answer each question by writing a complete sentence in French.)*

> **Modèle:** Il y a combien de chaises dans *(in)* la salle de classe?
> <u>Il y a quarante chaises dans la salle de classe</u>.

1. Il y a combien de **cahiers** dans la salle de classe?

   _____

2. Il y a combien de **livres** dans la bibliothèque?

   _____

3. Il y a combien d'**ordinateur**s dans le labo *(computer lab)*?

   _____

4. Il y a combien de **fenêtres** dans la salle de classe?

   _____

H How much do the following classroom items cost in euros? Answer each question by writing a complete sentence in French.

> **Modèle:** Combien coûte un livre?
> <u>Un livre coûte quinze euros</u>.

1. Combien coûte un crayon? _____

2. Combien coûte un ordinateur? _____

3. Combien coûte un stylo? _____

4. Combien coûtent deux stylos? _____

5. Combien coûtent cinq cahiers? _____

I *Parlons!* With a partner, see how good you are with numbers. Each of you receives 25 points at the beginning. Whenever either of you makes a mistake counting, subtract one point. To begin, you start counting from zero and then suddenly stop. Your partner must continue counting and then he or she may stop at any time. You should be quick enough to pick up where your partner leaves off. Continue counting and alternating until you reach 50 or another previously designated number. The player with more points at the end wins.

J Look at the clippings and answer the questions.

1. What is the most expensive travel destination?

   _____

2. What is the cost of a trip to *l'Algérie*?

   _____

3. The letter "j" stands for the French word for days, which is *jours*. How many days in Algeria does this trip offer? (*En français, s'il te plaît.*)

   _____

4. How many dishes are offered on the menu at this restaurant?

    _____

5. How many times does the letter "a" appear in the name of the restaurant?
    (*En français, s'il te plaît.*)

    _____

6. This is about a magazine subscription. What is the percentage (*pourcentage*) rate of the
    reduced price? (*En français, s'il te plaît.*)

    _____

7. How many issues does a subscriber receive for one year? (*En français, s'il te plaît.*)

    _____

8. *Quel est le prix pour un an* (year)? (Write out the number.)

    _____

9. Which French auto company makes the *Mégane?*

    _____

10. How much is the savings on the purchase price?

    _____

Unit 4

A **Match each city with its description.**

1. _____ Le Havre
2. _____ Nantes
3. _____ Lille
4. _____ Strasbourg
5. _____ Lyon

A. home of Duchess Anne of Brittany

B. transoceanic shipping port

C. site of two Roman amphitheaters

D. one of the capitals of the European Union

E. city with Flemish history

B **After studying the map of France and reading the information about French geography in your textbook, circle the letter of each correct answer.**

1. Which river starts in south-central France, flows north, and then turns west to the Atlantic?

   A. la Loire   B. la Seine   C. la Garonne

2. What is the name of the ocean west of France?

   A. l'Océan Indien   B. l'Océan Pacifique   C. l'Océan Atlantique

3. What is the name of the body of water between France and England?

   A. la Garonne   B. Nantes   C. la Manche

4. What is the name of a major mountain range?

   A. la Manche   B. les Pyrénées   C. Reims

5. Which river has its source in a Swiss glacier?

   A. la Seine   B. le Rhône   C. la Garonne

6. Which river divides France and Germany?

   A. le Rhône   B. la Garonne   C. le Rhin

7. Which river flows through the city of Paris?

   A. la Garonne   B. le Rhin   C. la Seine

8. Which river has its source in the Pyrenees Mountains?

   A. la Seine   B. la Garonne   C. le Rhône

C Look at the map of France in your textbook. Identify the general direction you travel from one city to another.

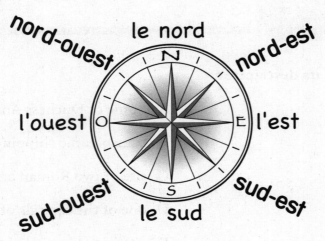

From	To	Direction
1. Lyon	Le Havre	_____
2. Reims	Strasbourg	_____
3. Lyon	Clermont-Ferrand	_____
4. Paris	Clermont-Ferrand	_____
5. Marseille	Lyon	_____
6. Biarritz	Bordeaux	_____
7. Lille	Nantes	_____
8. Biarritz	Marseille	_____

D Which name does not belong with the others? Circle the best choice in each group.

1. A. Lille   B. Nantes   C. la Seine

2. A. la Suisse   B. Lyon   C. l'Espagne

3. A. les Alpes   B. l'Océan Atlantique   C. la Mer Méditerranée

4. A. les Pyrénées   B. les Alpes   C. la Manche

5. A. la Manche   B. le Rhin   C. la Garonne

Nom: _____ Date: _____

E Look at the map of France. Identify the numbered cities and rivers on the map, and write their names in spaces 1–16 below. Each dot represents a city and each triangle represents a river.

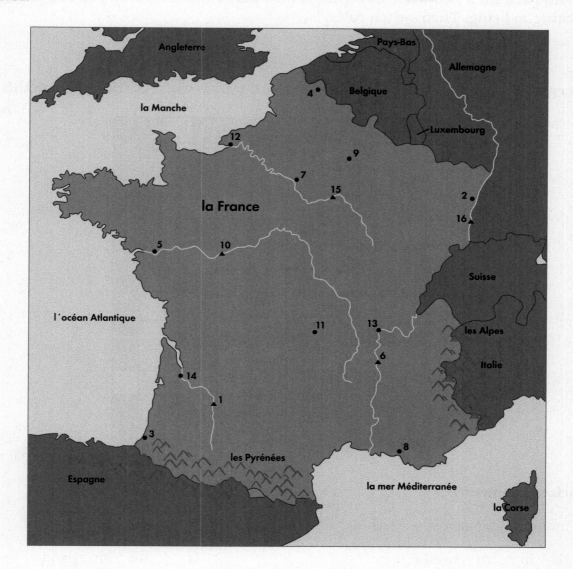

1. _____   9. _____

2. _____   10. _____

3. _____   11. _____

4. _____   12. _____

5. _____   13. _____

6. _____   14. _____

7. _____   15. _____

8. _____   16. _____

F *Parlons!* Imagine that you are inquiring at a travel agency about a trip to France. Ask your partner, a travel agent, about what you should see and do there. Also ask about what you should pack for a two-week stay. Decide on a particular month so you can plan what clothing to bring. Then switch roles.

G *Mots croisés.* Complete the following crossword puzzle with vocabulary from this unit.

Horizontalement

6. mountain range to the southeast

8. river in north central France

9. *la* ____, or Corsica

11. *l'*____, or Spain

12. river in southeastern France

13. river that divides Paris in two

14. *la* ____, or Belgium

Verticalement

1. *l'*____, or Italy

2. *la* ____, or Switzerland

3. *l'*____, or England

4. *l'*____, or Germany

5. English Channel

7. mountain range to the south

10. river in southwestern France

H **Review the clippings and answer the questions or provide the requested information.**

Le balisier est l'un des plus beaux ornements de la forêt dense.

Maroc

Guadeloupe. *Sur les pentes de la Soufrière, le parc national de l'île est un résumé des biotopes tropicaux : savanes d'altitude, forêt dense, jardins créoles...*

Corse

île et département français

Corse - Ile de Beauté

Les îles de Saint-Pierre et Miquelon

Bienvenue aux îles Saint-Pierre et Miquelon, où la France rencontre l'Amérique. Cinq cents ans d'histoire, un paysage naturel intact, de l'air pur, une hospitalité légendaire et surtout, la joie de vivre !

Où se trouve donc Saint-Pierre et Miquelon ?

L'archipel français de Saint-Pierre et Miquelon se trouve au sud de l'île canadienne de Terre-Neuve, à plus de 1800 kilomètres à l'Est de Montréal et 4300 km à l'Ouest

1. The word for island is *île*. Look over the clippings and find the names of four islands. What are they?

   _____

2. Which island is located in the Mediterranean Sea?

   _____

3. Which islands are located in the North Atlantic Ocean?

   _____

4. Which island is located in the Caribbean Sea?

   _____

5. Find the name of the country where *arabe* is spoken.

   _____

6. Give the English name of this country and its continent.

   _____

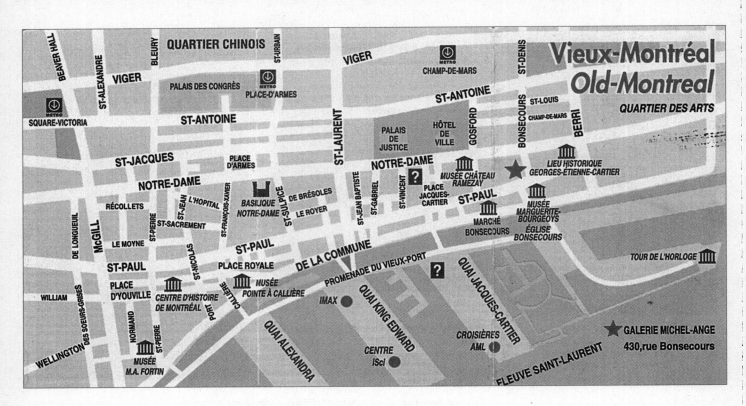

7. A wharf is a place where ships tie up to load and unload cargo. What is the French word for this place?

_____

8. What is the name of the river?

_____

9. The *Palais des Congrès* is located near which square, or *place*?

_____

10. Is the *Centre d'histoire de Montréal* close to Chinatown?

_____

11. Most of the streets and avenues have French names; name one that does not.

_____

Unit 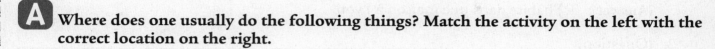 5

A **Where does one usually do the following things? Match the activity on the left with the correct location on the right.**

1. _____ cook
2. _____ sleep
3. _____ take a shower
4. _____ eat
5. _____ park the car
6. _____ plant flowers
7. _____ receive visitors

A. dans la salle de bains
B. dans le salon
C. dans la cuisine
D. dans la salle à manger
E. dans le jardin
F. dans la chambre
G. dans le garage

B **What would you logically find in each location? Circle the appropriate item.**

1. le salon:

   dishwasher   recliner   bathtub   car

2. la salle de bains:

   computer   blender   forks   shower

3. la cuisine:

   refrigerator   bed   car   toilet

4. la chambre:

   lawn mower   kitchen table   bedspread   washing machine

5. le garage:

   plates   lawnmower   pillowcases   bookcase

6. la salle à manger:

   broom   clothes closet   snow shovel   tablecloth

C Below are four answers to some missing questions. Think about the information given in these answers; then write the questions.

1. (Question): _____

   (Answer): J'habite dans une maison à Lyon.

2. (Question): _____

   (Answer): Il y a trois chambres dans l'appartement.

3. (Question): _____

   (Answer): La cuisine est derrière la salle à manger.

4. (Question): _____

   (Answer): Il y a une salle de bains dans ma maison.

D Complète le dialogue. *(Complete the dialogue in which Suzanne interviews Alex.)*

1. SUZANNE: Où habites-tu?

   ALEX: J'habite à _____. (city, town)

2. SUZANNE: Le garage, est-il derrière le jardin?

   ALEX: _____, le garage est là-bas.

3. SUZANNE: Il y a combien de chambres dans ta maison?

   ALEX: Il y a _____ chambres dans ma maison.

4. SUZANNE: Est-ce qu'il y a *(Is there)* un salon dans ta maison?

   ALEX: _____, naturellement!

5. SUZANNE: Il y a combien de salles de bains?

   ALEX: _____ une salle de bains.

6. SUZANNE: Est-ce qu'il y a des fleurs *(flowers)* dans le jardin?

   ALEX: Oui, il y des _____ dans le jardin.

E Find the way back to your bed. Name each type of house or shelter you encounter on your way.

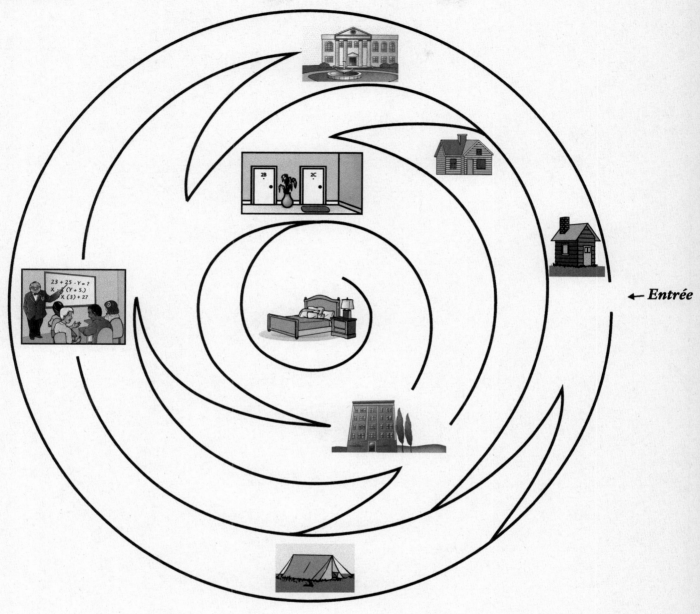

← *Entrée*

1. _____

2. _____

3. _____

4. _____

5. _____

Tu es architecte! *(Draw your own house plan, showing where all the rooms are. Label the rooms in French.)*

G *Parlons!* First, draw the floor plan of your **dream house** below. Then give your partner a tour of the house. Point to different rooms and other features, saying *Voici . . .* (Here is . . .) Your partner will then ask you the location of several rooms (*Où est . . . ?*) that you have not yet mentioned. When the tour is finished, the visitor says: *Ta maison est très belle. Merci beaucoup.* Then reverse roles, using your partner's floor plan.

H Review the clippings and answer the questions or provide the requested information.

Ma maison sur la Seine À PARIS, ON COMPTE PLUS DE 500 **PÉNICHES.** LA LISTE DES PRÉTENDANTS EST LONGUE CAR SELON CERTAINS, «VIVRE ICI N'A PAS DE PRIX» PAR BESMA LAHOURI

1. Many people enjoy living on barges. There are more than 500 of them in the area of the French capital. Find the word for "barges."

   _____

2. What river flows through this capital area?

   _____

3. What does the following sentence mean? *"Ma maison sur la Seine."*

   _____

   _____

4. This store sells furniture *(meubles)*. Look at the picture. *Il y a combien de meubles dans la pièce? (En français, s'il te plaît.)*

_____

5. Name the room for which this furniture would be appropriate. *(En français, s'il te plaît.)*

_____

6. Flowers always add to the atmosphere of a room. *Il y a des fleurs dans cette pièce?*

_____

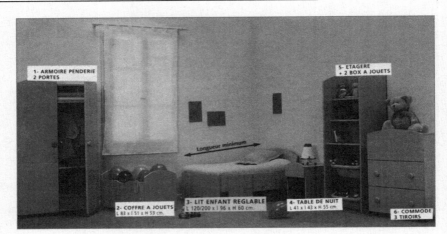

7. *Comment s'appelle la pièce?*

_____

8. What is standing next to the bed? *(En français, s'il te plaît.)*

_____

9. How do you say "Good night" in French?

_____

10. What does one put into an *armoire penderie*?

_____

11. Is the bed designed for an adult or a child?

_____

12. The *commode* has three *tiroirs*. What are *tiroirs*?

_____

Unit 6

A Match the English word with the French word(s).

1. _____ godparents
2. _____ girl
3. _____ baby
4. _____ boy
5. _____ niece
6. _____ aunt
7. _____ grandson
8. _____ nephew
9. _____ cousin
10. _____ uncle

A. le garçon
B. le petit-fils
C. l'oncle
D. le bébé
E. la cousine
F. le neveu
G. la tante
H. la nièce
I. la jeune fille
J. le parrain et la marraine

B Complète les phrases. *(Complete the sentences with the names of family members.)*

1. Le fils de mon frère est mon _____.

   neveu   oncle   cousin

2. La sœur de ma mère est ma _____.

   marraine   grand-mère   tante

3. Le fils de mes parents est mon _____.

   oncle   enfant   frère

4. Ma sœur est la _____ de mes grands-parents.

   jeune fille   petite-fille   fille

5. Le fils de mon oncle est mon _____.

   cousin   père   neveu

6. Ma mère est la _____ de mon père.

   femme   tante   marraine

7. La sœur de mon cousin est ma _____.

   tante   cousine   mère

8. La mère de mon père est ma _____.

   marraine   petite-fille   grand-mère

C **Draw a family picture (stick figures will be fine). Begin with yourself, adding the label** *C'est moi! Je m'appelle . . . .* **Add other family members:** *Voici (mon cousin, ma cousine, ma sœur, mon frère). Il/Elle s'appelle . . . .*

D In the spaces below, write in the names of your favorite television, movie, or storybook family. Use only the family members below that apply to your particular selection.

Name of TV show, movie, or book: _____

1. la mère _____

2. le père _____

3. le frère _____

4. la sœur _____

5. l'oncle _____

6. la tante _____

7. la grand-mère _____

8. le grand-père _____

E Combien de . . . ? *(Answer questions about your family.)*

> **Modèle:** Tu as combien de neveux *(nephews)*?
> Je n'ai pas de neveux.

1. Tu as combien de sœurs?

   _____

2. Tu as combien de tantes?

   _____

3. Tu as combien de frères?

   _____

4. Tu as combien de grands-parents?

   _____

5. Tu as combien d'oncles?

   _____

6. Tu as combien de cousines?

   _____

7. Tu as combien de cousins?

_____

8. Tu as combien de nièces?

_____

F *Mots croisés.* **Complete the following crossword puzzle with vocabulary from this unit.**

Horizontalement

3. female cousin

6. husband

7. stepmother

9. son

11. stepbrother

13. nephew

14. male cousin

15. daughter

16. aunt

Verticalement

1. wife or woman

2. godfather

4. uncle

5. baby

8. godmother

10. sister

12. child

G Make a list of the relatives in your nuclear family and in your extended family. State their relationship to you *(en français)* and their ages.

> **Modèles:**   Oncle Pierre, frère de Papa, 35 ans
> Aurélie, ma sœur, 15 ans

H Review the clippings and answer the questions or provide the requested information.

Une occasion unique de découvrir ou redécouvrir le Parc Disneyland® en famille ou entre amis !

This theme park, also called *Disneyland Resort Paris,* is just outside the capital.

1. Find the verbs that mean "discover" and "rediscover."

   _____

2. You are encouraged to visit the park *en famille* or *entre amis.* Explain what these phrases mean.

   _____

   Un enfant sur cent naît avec une malformation ou une maladie cardiaque.

   La Fondation québécoise pour les enfants malades du coeur soutient ces enfants et leurs parents.

   Aidez-nous à maintenir notre engagement en leur faveur.

3. The good health of a child depends on a healthy heart. Write in French: "one child."

   _____

4. Find the word for "heart." (Hint: look for the shape of the heart)

   _____

   en cœur.
   Depuis 1984
   1-800-EN COEUR
   www.fondationencoeur.com

5. The name of the island contains the name of certain family members. What is it? *(En français, s'il te plaît.)*

   _____

   À 5 minutes du centre-ville !

   Île des Soeurs

6. What is being advertised in this clipping?

   _____

   Location à partir de **549$** par mois !

   Le plus grand choix d'appartements et de maisons de ville à Montréal

   2 mois GRATUIT sur certaines unités

7. What is the name of the film?

_____

8. Where have you seen these words before?

_____

_____

Tel père, tel fils
Etats-Unis. 1986. Réalisation : Stuart Millar. 1 h 30.
Avec : Edward Asner, Gary Cole, Kate McNeil, Barbara Barrie.
Un chirurgien à qui tout réussit apprend que son père est devenu alcoolique. Cette révélation anéantit le brillant praticien. Rapidement, tout bascule autour de lui. Suivant le douloureux exemple d'un père, il ne tarde pas à sombrer dans la toxicomanie.
6201032

Les petits-fils
2004. 1h25. Comédie dramatique française en couleurs de Ilan Duran Cohen avec Reine Ferrato, Guillaume Quatravaux, Jean-Philippe Sêt, Brice Cauvin.
Une grand-mère et son petit-fils âgé de 24 ans vivent ensemble.

9. Complete this statement: The title *Les petits-fils* refers to whom?

_____

10. Name the two family members mentioned in the description of the movie.

_____

Unit  7

A **Dessine des images!** *(Draw pictures! As best you can, draw the animals listed below. Then label each one:* **C'est un/une . . . .** *If you have crayons or colored pencils, color your animals.)*

   1. la vache

                                 3. l'oiseau

   2. le chat

                                 4. le cheval

B **Je donne à manger à quels animaux?** *(Which animals am I feeding? Use the cues to guess the correct animal. Write each answer in the space provided.)*

   1. Arabian, Belgian, or Clydesdale

       Je donne à manger au _____.

   2. Wilbur or *The Three Little . . .*

       Je donne à manger au _____.

   3. Persian, Siamese, or Manx

       Je donne à manger au _____.

   4. Carrots, Thumper, or Bugs

       Je donne à manger au _____.

   5. German pointer, Irish setter, or Newfoundland

       Je donne à manger au _____.

   6. Blue jay, cardinal, or robin

       Je donne à manger à l'_____.

C **Line up these animals from biggest to smallest:**

> **un canard**   **un cheval**   **un cochon**   un chien

_____

_____

_____

_____

D **Complète les phrases en français.** *(Complete the sentences in French.)*

1. Yvette et Bertrand sont _____ campagne.

2. Il y a beaucoup *(many)* d'_____dans le pâturage.

3. La jeune fille a *(has)* une pomme pour le _____.

4. Le garçon peut tenir le _____ à la main.

5. Le cheval s'appelle _____.

E **Où sont les animaux? Complète les phrases en français.** *(Where are the animals? Complete each sentence by choosing the correct word from the word box. Notice the plural forms of each animal name!)*

> étang   **air**   **stalle**   p turage   **grange**

1. Les vaches sont dans le _____.

2. Les chevaux sont dans la _____.

3. Les poulets sont derrière la _____.

4. Les canards sont sur l'_____.

5. Les oiseaux sont dans l'_____.

F Les animaux, comment sont-ils? *(What are the animals like? Describe them as large or small.)*

> **Modèle:** Le chien Saint Bernard, comment est-il?
> <u>Le chien Saint Bernard est grand</u>.

Remember that a feminine, or *la* word, needs an *e* at the end of the adjective.
Remember that a plural word, or *les* word, needs an *s* at the end of the adjective.
If the plural noun is feminine, you must add an *e* before writing the *s*.

1. Le chien Chihuahua, comment est-il? _____

2. Le chat, comment est-il? _____

3. Le chat Garfield, comment est-il? _____

4. Les vaches, comment sont-elles? _____

5. Les ânes, comment sont-ils? _____

G Choose the correct meaning of each French sentence.

1. Je suis à la campagne.

   A. I am at camp.   B. I am in the country.

2. Je vois les canards.

   A. I see the ducks.   B. I'm feeding the ducks.

3. Je voudrais t'aider.

   A. I'd like to talk to you.   B. I'd like to help you.

4. Je donne à manger aux animaux.

   A. I am petting the animals.   B. I am feeding the animals.

5. Que fais-tu?

   A. What are you doing?   B. What do you have?

6. Je caresse mon lapin.

   A. I'm petting my rabbit.   B. I'm holding my pail.

H *Parlons!* Cut out pictures of animals introduced in this unit from magazines. Point to a picture and have your partner identify the animal. Then switch roles so that it is your turn to identify an animal.

I *C'est à toi!* If you find pictures of animals for which you do not know the name, look up what they are called in a French-English dictionary. Label all your pictures and then hang them on a classroom wall. Title your display *Les animaux.*

J *Les mots cachés.* Find and circle the French version of the words and expressions found on the right. Remember they may go forward, backward, up, down, or diagonally.

E	V	H	D	P	P	Z	I	I	S	F	U	E	O	H	P	L	F
E	D	X	Q	O	I	W	E	C	H	E	V	R	E	T	C	O	T
E	U	C	S	I	O	M	T	B	G	G	O	A	D	O	H	J	I
J	G	G	C	H	A	E	M	G	M	Z	D	A	B	H	T	W	T
B	S	N	H	D	K	N	B	N	B	Q	L	L	M	B	T	F	E
J	Y	L	I	C	A	G	A	F	F	I	D	K	O	Z	K	Q	P
E	Q	W	E	W	M	L	E	S	A	N	I	M	A	U	X	C	L
I	V	E	N	G	A	P	M	A	C	N	I	G	O	H	T	H	B
M	C	A	C	A	N	A	R	D	N	O	H	C	O	C	E	A	Z
N	F	Z	C	F	N	X	U	K	R	I	M	P	L	J	L	T	D
A	A	W	D	H	M	A	A	H	N	Z	Z	M	U	A	U	T	W
P	H	V	S	R	E	V	V	Z	I	C	S	A	D	G	O	E	G
N	T	X	S	S	G	Z	O	F	P	H	B	X	U	N	P	N	E
M	D	L	I	M	Q	E	N	A	A	E	Y	L	S	M	J	Y	R
F	Q	O	M	C	X	P	H	D	L	V	X	L	D	U	H	Q	C
Y	D	X	Q	D	J	W	H	Y	X	A	B	H	A	R	R	L	W
W	D	K	S	I	F	R	D	T	N	L	L	Q	T	G	L	I	T
R	F	H	A	U	Q	L	G	S	G	R	A	N	D	B	W	Y	A

1. donkey
2. cat
3. dog
4. rabbit
5. bird
6. cow
7. countryside
8. horse
9. pig
10. animals
11. small
12. duck
13. goat
14. big
15. eggs
16. chicken

K **Review the clippings and answer the questions.**

1. The restaurant is named after a certain lizard common to Central and South America. In French it is called *l'iguane.* What is the English (and Spanish) spelling of this word?

   _____

2. What kind of animal is *le pigeon?* *(En français, s'il te plaît.)*

   _____

3. What do you think the verb *vole* means?

   _____

4. A *chaton* is a young *chat.* How would you identify this young animal in English?

   _____

Pigeon vole. Fidèle en amour, cet oiseau a connu chez les éleveurs une infinité de métamorphoses. Il est l'ami volage des simples et des princes.

5. A teenager wants advice because he is being bitten and scratched by this pet. An animal expert suggests giving this young animal some toys to play with. How do you say "ping pong balls" in French?

   _____

6. The advice says you should be *patiente et calme avec ton animal.* What does that mean?

   _____

   _____

7. What is the name for a medical doctor who treats animals? (Hint: Look for a cognate.)

   _____

Comment faire pour que mon chaton cesse de me mordre et de me griffer ?

● D'abord, tu dois comprendre pourquoi ton chaton se comporte ainsi. Peut-être a-t-il été séparé trop tôt de ses frères et sœurs ? Peut-être joues-tu trop durement avec lui ? Commence par l'amuser autrement qu'avec tes doigts. Donne-lui des balles de ping-pong ou des boules de papier d'alu. Sois patiente et calme avec ton animal. Mais, si ses habitudes persistent, va consulter un vétérinaire.

Que peux-tu me dire sur les flamants roses ?

● Cet oiseau aux pattes démesurées, aux pieds palmés et au bec recourbé va bien ! On en compte un demi-million d'individus répartis en Afrique, en Asie du Sud-Ouest et au bord de la Méditerranée. On trouve ses colonies dans des lagunes d'eau salée peu profondes. Sa couleur rose vient des minuscules crevettes (les artémias), qu'il ingurgite chaque jour par milliers.

Le flamant aime faire le pied de grue dans la lagune.

8. What is the French word for "flamingo"?

   _____

9. About *un demi-million* are found around the world. What is the numerical equivalent of this number?

   _____

10. These birds live in shallow saltwater lagoons in warm climates. In what three geographical areas can they be found?

    _____

    _____

    _____

11. What type of body of water do flamingos seek out?

    _____

Unit 8

A Match the job titles on the left with the descriptions on the right.

1. _____ mécanicienne	A.	has a good sense of rhythm
2. _____ cuisinier	B.	knows how and when to plant crops
3. _____ électricien	C.	can help you take care of your health
4. _____ charpentier	D.	has a good sense of color and perspective
5. _____ médecin	E.	knows how to fix an engine
6. _____ acteur	F.	can create appetizing meals
7. _____ musicienne	G.	imitates gestures and memorizes words easily
8. _____ plombier	H.	knows hard wood from soft wood
9. _____ agricultrice	I.	knows how to install an electrical outlet
10. _____ artiste	J.	can repair a leaking faucet

B Circle the letter of the subject area most closely associated with each occupation.

1. le médecin

   A. anatomy   B. music   C. botany

2. la musicienne

   A. geography   B. fashion   C. band

3. l'agriculteur

   A. astronomy   B. soil analysis   C. literature

4. la commerçante

   A. drama   B. engineering   C. marketing

5. le cuisinier

   A. nutrition   B. history   C. math

6. l'actrice

   A. chemistry   B. physics   C. drama

Name the professional needed in each of the following circumstances. *Il faut téléphoner à* means "We must call . . . ."

> **Modèle:** Your parent's car will not start.
> <u>Il faut téléphoner à un mécanicien.</u>

1. You fell and injured your ankle.

   Il faut téléphoner à _____.

2. You need someone to paint your portrait as a surprise present for your parents.

   Il faut téléphoner à _____.

3. You and your family need someone to build new cabinets in the kitchen.

   Il faut téléphoner à _____.

4. You discover that the bathroom sink is clogged.

   Il faut téléphoner à _____.

5. You find that the lamp keeps flickering on and off.

   Il faut téléphoner à _____.

6. You need advice about how to make low-calorie meals.

   Il faut téléphoner à _____.

7. You are having trouble installing a new program on your computer.

   Il faut téléphoner à _____.

8. You are making a movie and need a woman to play a character.

   Il faut téléphoner à _____.

9. You invented a new product and need someone to sell it for you.

   Il faut téléphoner à _____.

10. Your grandfather is ill. Your family needs to find someone to take care of him during the day.

    Il faut téléphoner à _____.

D Complète le dialogue. *(Complete the dialogue by using the words in the box.)*

| facteur | cuisinière | profession | mécanicienne |
| travaille | quelle | emploi | infirmier | que | de |

1. FLORENCE: Quelle est ta _____?

2. ANTOINE: Je suis _____ à la poste.

3.   _____ fais-tu?

4. FLORENCE: Je _____ à un garage.

5.   Je suis _____.

6.   _____ est la profession de Monsieur Chardonne?

7. ANTOINE: Il est _____ dans un hôpital.

8.   Quelle est la profession _____ Claudine Brincourt?

9. FLORENCE: Elle est _____ dans un hôtel à Paris.

10. ANTOINE: Oh, mon parrain a aussi un _____ à Paris.

E *Parlons!* You and your partner first make a list of 10 cues in English. Each cue should correspond to one of the occupations you have learned in this unit. Then take turns telling one another the cues and guessing the associated occupations. If either person cannot correctly identify an occupation and its definite article on the first try, try again. You might like to compete with your partner. In that case, assign one point per correct article and one point per correct word. The winner is the first one who earns 20 points.

Modèles: A: orchestra
B. le musicien
A: Oui!

A: tractor
B: la cuisinière
A: Non!

F Complete these sentences with the names of occupations. The clues to help you are in the second sentence, which tells you where the person works. *Bonne chance!*

1. Je suis _____. Je travaille à la campagne.

2. Je suis _____. Je travaille dans un orchestre.

3. Je suis _____. Je travaille dans la cuisine.

4. Je suis _____. Je travaille à la poste.

5. Je suis _____. Je travaille au théâtre.

6. Je suis _____. Je travaille dans un hôpital.

7. Je suis _____. Je travaille dans un bureau.

G Choose an occupation from the list in your textbook. Then write in French what your occupation is and where you work. (See exercise F as a model.)

_____

_____

_____

_____

H *Mots croisés.* **Complete the following crossword puzzle with vocabulary from this unit.**

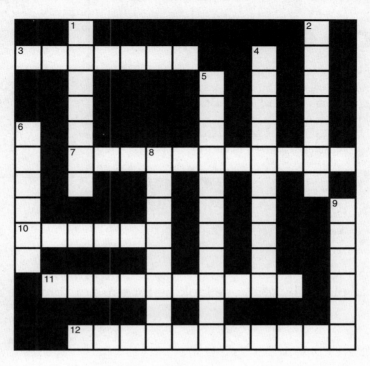

Horizontalement

3. sorts and distributes packages and letters (m.)

7. runs a business (f.)

10. job or work

11. prepares meals (f.)

12. *Que fais-tu pour _____?*
(to earn your living, 3 words)

Verticalement

1. performs a theatrical role (f.)

2. paints, draws, etches, or sculpts (m.+ f.)

4. *J'aime _____.* (to work)

5. frames a house (m.)

6. a word for "job" (requiring specific hands-on skills and technical training)

8. interprets musical scores (m.)

9. _____ *est ta profession?*

Nom: _____   Date: _____

 Review the clippings and answer the questions.

FORMATION: COIFFEUR

Vous rêvez d'ouvrir un salon de coiffure afin d'offrir des métamorphoses beauté à vos clientes et ainsi faire ressortir la beauté de leurs traits et l'unicité de leur personnalité? Voici les bonnes étapes pour devenir un pro du ciseau!

ECRIVAINS

Les Editions du Panthéon
recherchent de nouveaux talents pour leurs collections littéraires.
Envoyez vos manuscrits inédits ou écrivez aux
Editions du Panthéon - Service ML, 27, cité industrielle - 75011 Paris
Tél. 01 43 71 14 72 - Fax : 01 43 71 14 46

Les éditions du
PANTHEON

Code de la Propriété intellectuelle. Art. L. 132-2

OFFRES D'EMPLOI

108 GARDERIES/ENFANTS
ÉDUCATRICE auprès des enfants (0-4ans) dans halte-garderie d'un org. communautaire pour jeunes mères. De sept. à juin, 40h/sem. de jour, 13.50$/h. Remplacement de congé de maternité. Formation: Éduc. spécialisée, tech. d'éduc. à l'enfance ou domaine connexe Cv avant 31août au : Petit REVDEC, 4551 Lafontaine, Mtl, Que, H1V 1P6 ou courriel: revdec@cam.org

 **Prenez votre carrière en main**

1. Is an *offre d'emploi* placed by someone looking for work or someone advertising a job vacancy?

    _____

2. An organization is looking for an *éducatrice* who must have special training in *éducation à l'enfance* or a similar background. What will this person do?

    _____

3. A *coiffure* is a hairstyle. What do you think a *coiffeur* does as a job?

    _____

4. The occupational title of *écrivain* is related to a word you know, *Écris*. What do you think an *écrivain* does for a living?

    _____

5. The *écrivain* can work at a place such as *Les éditions du Panthéon*. Is this company a school or a publishing company?

    _____

6. *Prenez votre carrière en main* suggests that you start to get serious about something. What?

    _____

Unit  9

A Circle the letter of what you would logically choose in each situation.

1. You are thirsty.

   A. les biscuits   B. le fromage   C. le poivre   D. le jus

2. You are hungry.

   A. l'eau minérale   B. le sel   C. le déjeuner   D. la serviette

3. You want to eat fruit.

   A. du poulet   B. des poires   C. du beurre   D. du pain

4. You are going to have some soup and need a utensil.

   A. une cuiller   B. une soucoupe   C. une nappe   D. un couteau

5. You want some dessert.

   A. des épinards   B. du saucisson   C. de la glace   D. du lait

B You are having guests for a special dinner this evening. Create a menu. (En français, s'il te plaît.)

1. Appetizer: Biscuits salés (crackers) et _____

2. Main dish or specialty: _____

3. Vegetables (3): _____, _____, _____

4. Salad: _____

5. Dessert: _____

6. Beverages (2): _____ et _____

C **Match the descriptions on the left with the items on the right.**

1. _____ seasoning for meat or vegetables

2. _____ bread spread

3. _____ container for milk or juice

4. _____ sweetener

5. _____ cutting utensil

6. _____ container for coffee or tea

7. _____ first meal of the day

8. _____ utensil for eating soup

9. _____ table covering

10. _____ midday meal

A. le sucre

B. la tasse

C. le verre

D. le déjeuner

E. la cuiller

F. le sel

G. le petit déjeuner

H. le couteau

I. le beurre

J. la nappe

D **Circle the letter that contains the answer to the question.**

1. What are the main ingredients in *la soupe à l'oignon?*

   A. chicken and mushrooms

   B. rice and tomatoes

   C. onions and cheese

2. What does *la charlotte aux framboises* contain?

   A. sponge cake, custard, and raspberies

   B. pasta, tomatoes, and spinach

   C. roast duck and orange marmalade

3. What are *crêpes bretonnes?*

   A. chicken sandwiches

   B. thin pancakes

   C. scrambled eggs and sausage

4. What are the main ingredients in *la ratatouille?*

   A. macaroni and cheese

   B. beef and potatoes

   C. eggplant and zucchini

5. What is *la tarte aux myrtilles?*

   A. a blueberry dessert

   B. a chocolate cake

   C. a banana cream pie

6. How is *le canard à l'orange* prepared?

   A. fried

   B. roasted

   C. boiled

7. What does *la quiche lorraine* contain?

   A. hazelnuts and chocolate

   B. spinach, beans, and tomatoes

   C. bacon, onions, and cheese

8. In what part of France did *le cassoulet* first become very popular?

   A. southwestern

   B. central

   C. southeastern

9. What city is most closely associated with *la bouillabaisse?*

   A. Le Havre

   B. Nantes

   C. Marseille

10. What is in the dish called *le gratin savoyard?*

    A. chicken and vegetables

    B. potatoes and cheese

    C. beef soup with crackers

E *Les mots cachés.* **Find and circle the French version of the words and expressions listed on the right. Remember they may go forward, backward, up, down, or diagonally.**

```
J  S  I  S  V  D  C  T  D  L  O  C  U  I  S  I  N  E
V  F  E  N  C  S  E  U  F  H  Z  R  E  L  L  I  U  C
G  L  K  R  S  O  U  Z  G  S  N  H  T  B  W  G  R  G
G  G  E  E  O  I  N  F  V  E  W  D  F  A  I  M  F  C
L  M  Z  V  R  F  A  A  F  T  T  Z  G  A  R  T  O  M
V  A  F  O  U  R  C  H  E  T  T  E  L  M  O  U  Z  I
F  Y  R  A  S  O  H  I  T  E  A  U  C  X  T  X  H  D
C  X  F  R  F  S  A  E  D  I  T  L  R  E  E  G  V  Y
A  F  Q  I  W  E  I  U  V  S  R  I  A  R  R  S  W  T
V  W  E  P  K  R  M  A  R  S  Y  U  U  E  Y  S  I  V
E  V  J  Q  E  R  I  N  J  A  D  T  G  I  U  T  X  N
R  E  T  C  J  C  B  R  J  T  I  N  E  C  E  X  T  U
R  X  I  R  E  K  H  V  G  R  A  N  R  P  W  L  G  G
E  P  Y  N  D  R  I  N  R  M  Y  E  P  O  I  V  R  E
E  W  J  H  L  R  B  U  F  A  M  A  P  F  U  D  P  R
D  H  R  W  B  M  O  A  H  B  N  I  F  Y  Y  Y  D  W
W  F  J  Y  I  N  T  J  P  O  U  Y  B  K  O  L  D  M
Z  R  Q  E  L  M  N  H  B  I  G  F  M  Y  F  J  W  H
```

1. plate
2. spoon
3. hungry
4. food
5. thirsty
6. Enjoy your meal!
7. cooking
8. fork
9. pepper
10. sugar
11. knife
12. grocery store
13. to eat
14. salt
15. glass

F Set the table by drawing on it all the items below. Make sure you have a nice *crayon* with an eraser. You are the *artiste* now. After you draw an item, check it off the list. If you run out of space on your table, don't worry. Try to draw as many of the items as you can. Neatness counts, so take your time and make an attractive table.

Check list

une nappe _____✓_____

une assiette _____

une fourchette _____

un couteau _____

une cuiller _____

une cuiller à café _____

une serviette _____

un verre _____

une tasse _____

une soucoupe _____

un vase _____

le beurre _____

le poivre _____

le sel _____

G *Parlons!* Draw the utensils and foods and beverages of this unit. Show each one to your partner, asking what it is. He/she will answer in French. If the answer is incorrect, you must correct the error. When your partner has identified all the pictures, change roles. Now, you answer each question. (Be sure to put *un* or *une* before the noun.)

Modèles:	You:	Qu'est-ce que c'est? (showing picture of a glass)
	Your partner:	C'est un verre.
	You:	Oui.
	Your partner:	Qu'est-ce que c'est? (showing picture of a spoon)
	You:	C'est un couteau.
	Your partner:	Non, c'est une cuiller.

H Your friend invites you home for a snack. Ask in French what there is to eat. You will get a choice of three fruits, some cookies, or ice cream. Say *"Bon. J'ai faim. Merci."* Then select one of the items that your partner offered. *(En français, s'il te plaît.)*

I Review the clippings and answer the questions.

• Rouleaux aux avocats • Salade asiatique
• Gâteau au fromage framboises & chocolat blanc
. . . et plus de 120 plats délicieux.

1. A restaurant recommends the *rouleaux aux avocats* (avocado slices) followed by the *salade asiatique*. If you are familiar with oriental foods, you might be able to suggest some foods that would be included in this salad. Any ideas?

   _____

2. What words say "raspberry cheesecake" and "white chocolate"?

   _____

3. At this restaurant you will also find more than 120 *plats délicieux*. What do you think these are?

   _____

4. How is restaurant abbreviated?

   _____

5. In what two areas in this restaurant can you dine?

   _____

6. Does this restaurant offer counter or sit-down service? How is this type of service described?

   _____

7. Does it make deliveries?

   _____

**Resto-bar
Terrasse
Salle à manger
Comptoir
service rapide
Livraison**

8. What is a *recette*?

   _____

9. *Maïs* means corn. What does the *recette* make?

   _____

10. What is the French word that identifies this type of food?

   _____

11. *La recette, c'est pour combien de personnes? (En français, s'il te plaît.)*

   _____

RECETTE **EXPRESS**

Chowder de maïs

Pour moi, les chowders de maïs, avec toutes leurs variations, sont les soupes de la rentrée. C'est une très bonne façon de traiter le maïs qu'on ne fait pas bouillir mais qu'on fait sauter au beurre ou à l'huile. Et pourquoi pas? Ça nous change de la méthode à l'eau et ça lui donne un goût caramélisé tout à fait délicieux. En plus, c'est très facile à faire et ça surprend toujours.

Pour 4 personnes

INGRÉDIENTS:
> 1 c. à soupe d'huile d'olive extra-vierge
> 1 oignon émincé
> 1 gousse d'ail émincée
> 1 c. à thé de gingembre frais râpé
> 1 pincée de poudre de curry (facultative) ou du ras-el-hanout frais
> 1 c. à thé de muscade fraîchement râpée
> 4 épis de maïs, les grains retirés à l'aide d'un couteau
> 500 ml de bouillon de volaille de qualité
> 1 tasse de lait de coco en boîte (vendu dans les épiceries asiatiques. Prenez une marque qui ne contient pas d'additifs)
> 100 g de viande de caille ou de canard ou de crabe cuit, effilochée
> Huile d'olive extra-vierge pour la garniture
> Quelques feuilles de coriandre ou de persil, finement hachées

12. *Comment s'appelle le restaurant?*

   _____

13. What does *fine cuisine française* mean?

   _____

14. Van Houtte Café offers meals at times convenient to you!
    What are the four times during the day when different menus
    are prepared? *(En anglais, s'il te plaît.)*

   _____

   _____

   _____

Unit 10

A **Complete each sentence by writing the name of the appropriate artist.**

1. If you like paintings with historical subjects, you might like some of the paintings

   by _____.

2. If you like seeing pictures of people doing outdoor activities, you might enjoy the artwork

   by _____.

3. If you like horses in particular, you might like to view some of the paintings

   by _____.

4. If you like animals in general, you might appreciate the etchings and paintings

   by _____.

5. If you like contemporary sculptures in marble, glass, and stone, you might like to view the

   work by _____.

B **Write the name of the artist associated with the style on the left.**

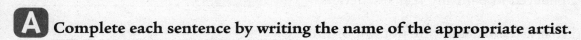

Eugène Delacroix   Françoise Gilot   Jacques Louis David   Édouard Manet

1. Impressionism   _____

2. Modern art   _____

3. Classicism   _____

4. Romanticism   _____

C **Name the artist who . . .**

1. . . . tried to show motion, such as that by galloping horses. _____

2. . . . strongly believed in painting realistic details. _____

3. . . . believed that artistic details are not important. _____

4. . . . used Egyptian themes. _____

5. . . . united time and space in a series of shadows and arches. _____

6. . . . was influenced by the work of Pablo Picasso. _____

D *Je suis artiste!* **This is the place where you get to be an artist. Don't worry if you are not artistic. (Perhaps you are more of a cubist or abstract painter than a conventional painter!) The list below represents your drawing assignments. Draw four of the items listed. When you are done, exchange your drawings with a partner and ask him or her to write a description or title for each one.**

1. un livre d'art ouvert *(open)*

2. un ordinateur dans un cyber café

3. une tente à la campagne

4. une cabane dans un bois *(woods)*

5. un chien dans le parc

6. une table dans la salle à manger

7. un réfrigérateur ouvert

8. la chambre d'un(e) adolescent(e)

Now draw a picture to show what each sentence means.

1. Élisabeth donne une pomme au cheval.

2. Sara parle avec le facteur.

3. Jean-Luc caresse le chat.

4. Il y a des devoirs *(homework)* et une pomme sur le bureau du prof.

Nom: _____ Date: _____

F *Les mots cachés.* **Find and circle the words and expressions in English found on the right. Remember they may go forward, backward, up, down, or diagonally.**

J	L	S	C	K	C	F	D	O	L	O	X	L	X	D	M	X	H	R
G	P	Q	X	G	D	L	L	T	M	D	K	U	D	L	A	I	G	Q
Y	Z	O	T	O	N	V	G	O	J	N	B	Z	V	F	M	C	E	B
E	R	L	F	V	C	I	O	B	W	H	B	B	T	G	G	F	Z	I
L	N	L	U	X	T	Y	T	O	Q	I	S	E	Q	J	Y	Y	C	M
R	B	W	R	B	V	B	G	N	I	N	P	I	C	T	U	R	E
H	U	U	H	T	L	R	R	L	I	A	H	G	D	C	A	N	L	D
C	T	F	A	T	C	X	J	O	M	A	I	J	L	A	Q	C	H	N
L	B	M	G	M	I	M	G	W	L	X	P	A	J	I	V	R	S	R
A	I	F	Y	M	J	U	J	W	R	O	X	L	U	K	N	I	J	A
S	E	X	I	O	R	C	A	L	E	D	C	Q	I	C	E	E	D	E
S	R	U	R	O	M	A	N	T	I	C	I	S	M	K	I	I	S	L
I	U	T	G	Z	P	W	R	S	T	O	M	Y	F	J	N	A	O	C
C	T	H	W	X	D	O	G	T	M	C	V	C	F	V	J	M	Y	D
I	P	N	S	G	T	D	M	G	D	W	M	O	K	Q	L	T	F	F
S	L	H	M	S	I	N	O	I	S	S	E	R	P	M	I	U	U	A
M	U	B	T	J	G	J	P	M	N	J	Z	U	Y	A	Z	S	O	C
M	C	C	K	F	P	O	I	I	E	S	S	L	F	Z	S	L	D	S
Y	S	A	X	Q	J	M	L	J	R	G	T	W	Y	V	E	R	U	E

1. art
2. color
3. flowing lines
4. Manet
5. romanticism
6. classicism
7. David
8. fuzzy
9. painting
10. sculpture
11. clear
12. Delacroix
13. impressionism
14. picture

G *C'est à toi!* **Of the all the artwork presented in this unit, decide which one is your favorite. Your teacher will designate a corner or a spot in your classroom for a discussion of each painting. Go to the area where your favorite artwork will be discussed. Find out why everyone likes this picture the best. Write down the reasons. Choose a spokesperson to report your reasons to the entire class. Listen to what all the groups have to say and write down the results. What can you say about the artistic tastes of your class? For example, are they varied, predictable, surprising?**

H **Review the clippings and answer the questions or provide the information requested.**

1. An advertisement for food uses the word *l'art* in an extended sense. What is *l'art culinaire?*

_____

2. *Le Chariot* promotes itself as the largest gallery of Inuit (Eskimo-Native American) art in the country. Name the country where the gallery is located.

_____

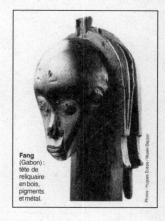

3. The wooden head is part of an exhibit of Fang art from Africa. The Fang people live in Gabon. This piece is an example of reliquary art, that is, works of art that were once placed in the tombs of deceased family members. The word for wood is *bois*. Find two materials other than wood that were used to make this piece.

_____

4. *Comment s'appelle la galerie d'art?*

_____

5. *"Giraffe," c'est aussi* (also) *le nom d'un* . . .

_____

6. Art from what region is exhibited in this gallery?

_____

7. The word *Trésors* is close to an English word. What do you think
   it means?

   _____

8. What is the museum's name?

   _____

9. Is this an art museum?

   _____

10. What are the four words that mean "a bridge to history"?

   _____

TRÉSORS
DU MUSÉE STEWART

UN PONT VERS L'HISTOIRE

Le Fort, Île Sainte-Hélène
Parc Jean-Drapeau
20 mai - 9 octobre :
tous les jours, de 10 h à 17 h
Hors saison :
10 h à 17 h, fermé les mardis
Stationnement (P7).
Info : (514) 861-6701
www.stewart-museum.org

PEINTURE
Toute la palette des Mille et Une Nuits

Au siècle des Lumières, l'Orient
fait irruption dans l'art. D'abord
en quête d'exotisme fantaisiste,
les peintres cherchent bientôt
l'émotion des paysages et des
couleurs de ce Moyen-Orient
bariolé, violent et sensuel, dé-
couvert avec la campagne
de Napoléon en Egypte. Plus de
trois cents illustrations en couleurs composent un parcours
chronologique et géographique
dans un Orient toujours rêvé.
«L'Univers des Orientalistes»
Gérard-Georges Lemaire

11. The word *peinture* is an art-related word. What do you think it means?

   _____

12. Complete the title *L'univers des . . .*

   _____

13. The title refers to the French artists who used *le Moyen-Orient* for artistic inspiration. Where
    is *le Moyen-Orient?*

   _____

14. What does an artist put on a *palette?*

   _____

15. This book is described as being as colorful as the famous story "A Thousand and One
    Nights." Find the French version of this name.

   _____

Unit 11

A Match the English body part on the left with its French equivalent on the right.

1. _____ hair   A. le pied
2. _____ nose   B. l'oreille
3. _____ foot   C. le genou
4. _____ chest   D. la tête
5. _____ neck   E. le nez
6. _____ elbow   F. la poitrine
7. _____ ear   G. le cou
8. _____ eye   H. le coude
9. _____ knee   I. les cheveux
10. _____ head   J. l'œil

B Match each command on the left with the body part(s) you need to complete it.

1. _____ Va au tableau!   A. la main
2. _____ Écris!   B. les yeux
3. _____ Lis!   C. les pieds
4. _____ Écoute!   D. la bouche
5. _____ Parle!   E. les oreilles

C Fill in the missing letter to complete each expression.

1. l'œ_l   4. le __ou   7. le fr__nt

2. la de__t   5. la bo__che   8. l' __stomac

3. le ge__ou   6. la figu__e   9. la jam__e

D **Answer each question with an appropriate body part in French. Don't forget to include the article.**

1. What tells you that something is baking in the oven? _____

2. What needs calcium to make them strong? _____

3. What do you open at dinnertime? _____

4. What two things bend to help you sit down? _____

5. What do you use to throw a ball? _____

6. What do you use to play the piano? _____

7. What should you protect from loud noises? _____

8. What do you move to say the letters "m" and "b"? _____

9. What has a cornea and an iris? _____

10. What part of your body stores your brain? _____

E **Complète en français. (*Complete the sentences in French with the words for the appropriate body parts.*)**

1. Le _____ est au-dessus de *(above)* la bouche.

2. La _____ est entre *(between)* le cou et l'estomac.

3. Le _____ est entre les épaules.

4. Le _____ est entre l'épaule et la main.

5. Le _____ est au milieu de *(in the middle of)* la jambe.

6. L' _____ est au milieu du corps.

7. Le _____ est au-dessus des yeux.

8. Dans la _____ il y a deux yeux, un nez, et une bouche.

9. Il y a cinq _____ sur *(on)* la main.

10. Il y trente-deux _____ dans *(in)* la bouche.

F Arrange the words, expressions, and sentences under the appropriate column: Positive or Negative. Positive = words that convey the *positive* feelings of health and happiness Negative = words that convey the *negative* feelings of illness and unhappiness

> malade Je vais bien. Je ne vais pas bien. triste Je me sens mal. en bonne santé Je me sens bien. heureux (heureuse)

Positive ☺

Negative ☹

_____ _____

_____ _____

_____ _____

_____ _____

G Complète les phrases en français. *(Complete the sentences in French.)*

1. JEAN-PAUL: Je suis malade.

   HÉLÈNE: Qu'est-ce que tu _____? *(What's wrong?)*

   JEAN-PAUL: J'ai mal à la _____. *(head)*

2. MARIE-ÉLISE: Je ne vais pas bien.

   JEAN-PIERRE: Qu'est-ce que _____ as? *(you)*

   MARIE-ÉLISE: J'ai la _____. *(flu)*

3. SUZANNE: Comment vas-tu?

   DOMINIQUE: _____ vais bien.

4. BABETTE: Comment est-ce que tu te sens?

   CLAUDETTE: Je me _____ bien.

5. FRANÇOIS: Tu es en bonne santé?

   FRANÇOISE: Non, je suis _____. *(sick)*

H Écris en français:

1. I'm feeling fine. _____

2. I'm feeling awful. _____

3. I'm happy. _____

4. I'm sad. _____

I *Parlons!* Working in pairs, practice the French names for the parts of the body. Use a doll, a teddy bear, a picture, or yourselves. Taking turns, each of you should point to a part of the body and ask your partner what it is. The other one should answer. Then ask if that body part belongs to the face or body.

> **Modèle:** A: Qu'est-ce que c'est?
> B: C'est une épaule.
>
> A: C'est une partie de la figure ou du corps?
> B: C'est une partie du corps.

J In the space provided, draw a person, one part of the body at a time. Working in pairs, your partner announces a part of the body, for example, *le pied,* and you draw it. Continue until the picture is completed. You might try drawing a cat or another animal, but you may have to look up some French words, such as "tail" and "paw," etc.

K *Mots croisés.* **Complete the following crossword puzzle with vocabulary from this unit.**

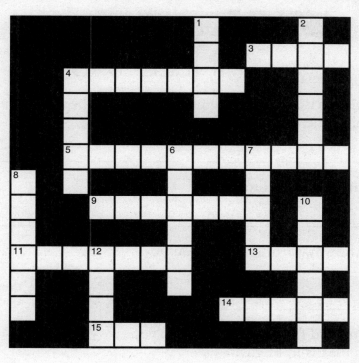

Horizontalement

3. *Je _____ bien.*

4. covers *la tête*

5. toe

9. lets us hear sounds

11. _____ *tu te sens?* (How do you feel?)

13. *Je _____ heureux.*

14. body

15. lets us smell odors and fragrances

Verticalement

1. *un œil + un œil = deux _____*

2. face

4. between your shoulder and your hand

6. sad

7. at the end of our *jambes*

8. contains our teeth and our tongue

10. flu

12. used to hold a pen or a fork

L Review the clippings and answer the questions or provide requested information.

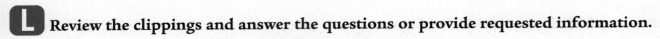

RENTRÉE SCOLAIRE SANS FUMÉE

FINI LE TABAC

1. A health warning advises that young people who have begun to smoke should kick the habit by a certain time. When is recommended?

   _____

2. Find two smoking-related words.

   _____

3. What does this health warning advise you not to do?

   _____

Contre la **Toast** Attitude,
le conseil soleil du jour :

Peaux jeunes
=peaux fragiles

recommandé par l'Institut National du Cancer

4. You have a young and fragile *peau*. What do you think this word means in English?

   _____

5. How much fat does the energy bar contain?

   _____

Barres tendres d'énergie

Moins de 3 grammes
de gras par barre

6. What is the metric unit of measurement *en français*?

   _____

7. What is the word for "fatty"?

   _____

8. Into what category of food can *pommes* and *cassis* (currants) be classified?

   _____

A LA COMPOTE DE POMMES FRAICHES

POMME·CASSIS

ANDROS

9. A dessert of stewed fruit has a special name. Find this name.

   _____

10. *Les pommes, sont-elles fraîches? (En français, s'il te plaît.)*

   _____

Unit 12

A Match the description on the left with the French article of clothing on the right.

1. _____ a woman's attire when dressing up   A. le blouson

2. _____ formal outfit for a man   B. la cravate

3. _____ bedtime attire   C. la ceinture

4. _____ worn around the neck   D. la robe

5. _____ worn often with a skirt   E. le costume

6. _____ casual and trendy headwear   F. le chemisier

7. _____ basic covering for the head   G. le chapeau

8. _____ short jacket   H. le manteau

9. _____ overcoat or long coat   I. la casquette

10. _____ worn to hold up trousers   J. la robe de chambre

B Circle the expression that does not belong with the others.

1.	les gants	le manteau	le pyjama
2.	la casquette	le chemisier	le chapeau
3.	le mouchoir	la jupe	le pantalon
4.	la robe	la chemise	la cravate
5.	la chemise	le chemisier	la casquette

C **Name in French the article of clothing that you would logically wear in the following situations.**

1. You are cold and have your pajamas on.

   _____

2. You are about to build a snowman and want to protect your hands.

   _____

3. You are going to sneeze.

   _____

4. Your pants are too loose.

   _____

5. You are going to a baseball game and will be out in the sun.

   _____

6. You want to walk to the store in these.

   _____

D **What's the price? Finish each sentence with the French word for each item in parentheses. Remember to begin with the article.**

1. Combien coûte _____? *(blouse)*

2. Combien coûte _____? *(suit)*

3. Combien coûte _____? *(dress)*

4. Combien coûtent _____? *(shoes)*

5. Combien coûtent _____? *(socks)*

E Find your way through the clothing store. Name the articles of clothing that you encounter on the way.

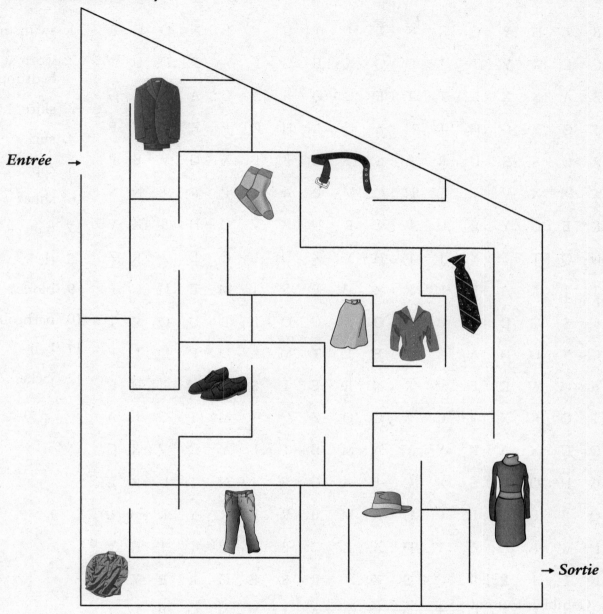

Entrée →

→ *Sortie*

1. _____

2. _____

3. _____

4. _____

5. _____

6. _____

F *Les mots cachés.* **Find and circle the French version of the words and expressions on the right. Remember they may go forward, backward, up, down, or diagonally.**

K	C	B	Z	H	Y	G	K	N	L	I	J	U	P	E	N	O	C	R
B	C	C	E	W	T	J	D	Q	X	L	G	F	A	P	H	U	W
Q	W	B	A	S	X	E	T	T	E	U	Q	S	A	C	A	X	R	G
X	N	J	G	X	D	H	I	H	A	U	L	H	D	P	B	P	V	F
C	H	A	U	S	S	U	R	E	S	J	G	F	E	X	G	V	B	P
A	I	W	M	X	V	J	T	N	O	M	R	A	I	P	R	I	N	S
M	I	K	E	G	Y	E	U	P	C	R	U	B	V	O	H	S	K	V
A	P	N	Q	T	I	Y	J	P	H	Y	X	U	L	O	E	Z	R	Z
J	E	J	J	X	A	X	L	R	Z	M	E	S	I	M	E	H	C	P
Y	I	K	S	G	D	V	B	N	O	S	U	O	L	B	U	O	P	T
P	N	C	Y	D	H	A	A	J	F	L	T	M	K	D	F	D	L	F
I	A	F	U	W	K	F	M	R	N	R	E	I	S	I	M	E	H	C
E	F	I	O	K	X	V	C	Z	C	O	Z	Q	W	M	T	G	E	A
P	I	O	U	X	A	K	Y	Y	A	M	E	T	L	Y	D	V	S	G
A	H	G	H	O	L	S	X	C	I	A	C	E	I	N	T	U	R	E
B	R	O	B	E	D	E	C	H	A	M	B	R	E	R	Y	R	M	L
Z	C	N	W	P	D	O	T	D	A	A	O	B	U	T	I	J	H	V
Z	X	H	L	I	E	R	Q	C	U	J	P	S	E	Q	R	E	Y	H
W	M	A	I	L	L	O	T	D	E	B	A	I	N	N	M	P	V	I

1. swimsuit
2. worn at bedtime
3. skirt
4. shirt
5. cap
6. shoes
7. hat
8. tie
9. blouse
10. bathrobe
11. belt
12. jacket

G *Parlons!* Who wears what and where? Begin by thinking of five occupations in French from Unit 8.

Step 1: As you say the name of each occupation, your partner will say one item of work clothing typically worn by that person. You keep track of how many of your partner's answers are correct.

> **Modèle:**   You: *charpentier*
>   Your partner: *chaussures*
> (This is a correct response, so your partner earns one point. If he answered *jupe,* that would be incorrect and he/she would not earn a point.)

Step 2: Next, your partner says five articles of clothing. You must respond with a place where one might wear each item.

> **Modèle:**   Partner: *cravate*
>   You: formal dinner
> (You earn a point. The winner is the player with more points.)

H Complète les dialogues. *(Complete the dialogues by selecting the correct words from the word box. One word in each dialogue will not be used.)*

Dialogue 1

> **concert**   **pyjama**   costume

MARC: Que portes-tu?

PHILIPPE: Je porte mon nouveau _____.

MARC: Pourquoi?

PHILIPPE: Je vais ce soir à un _____.

Dialogue 2

> **jardin**   **cravate**   **blouson**

MARIE: Que portes-tu, Simone?

SIMONE: Un _____.

MARIE: Pourquoi?

SIMONE: Je vais dans le _____.

Dialogue 3

salle de bains   robe de chambre   chapeau

GILLES: Que portes-tu, Georges?

GEORGES: Ma _____.

GILLES: Pourquoi?

GEORGES: Je vais en ce moment à la _____.

Dialogue 4

belle   beau

CLAIRE: Comment est la robe?

ROSANNE: Elle est _____.

Dialogue 5

petites   petits

ÉRIC: Comment sont les chaussures?

SANDRINE: Elles sont _____.

I **Review the clippings and answer the questions or provide the requested information.**

À ne pas manquer,
faites de RITSI
votre destination pour
collections haut de gamme,
spécialisées
dans les tailles 6 à 24

RITSI

Tailles/sizes 6 - 24

4863 Sherbrooke Ouest • Westmount, Québec
Tél. (514) 481-8600 • Fax (514) 481-4130

1. This store carries a wide range of clothing sizes. Find the word for sizes.

   _____

2. Express the range of sizes in French.

   _____

POUR LUI
Il est toujours plus difficile de dénicher un cadeau qui saura plaire
à notre tendre moitié, ou à notre cher papa ou encore pour le grand
de la famille, mais avec Montréal vous n'aurez pas
ce problème !

Globo
Basket
49,99$

Pêle-mêle de 50$ à
votre limite de budget

vêtements prêts-à-
porter ou griffes
québécoises, montres,
chaussures, articles de
sport, accessoires,
etc.

3. What kind of shoe is this?

   _____

4. *Combien coûte une paire de chaussures?*

   _____

5. Clothing that is not specially designed and custom tailored for an individual is called
   "ready-to-wear." Find the words that say this.

   _____

To answer questions 6 through 9, choose A (the girl on the left) or B (the girl on the right).

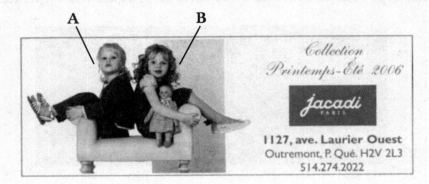

6. *Quelle* (Which) *fille porte une robe?*

   _____

7. *Quelle fille porte un pantalon?*

   _____

8. *Quelle fille porte des sandales?*

   _____

9. *Quelle fille porte une chemise?*

   _____

10. Is this woman's black beach dress available in white also?
    (En français, s'il te plaît.)

    _____

Unit 13

A **Answer each question by circling the appropriate letter.**

1. At what time does the sun rise?

   A. à six heures deux

   B. à midi

2. At what time does the sun set?

   A. à une heure

   B. à sept heures onze

3. At what time do you leave for school in the morning?

   A. à quatre heures et quart

   B. à huit heures et quart

4. At what time are you dismissed from school every day?

   A. à trois heures

   B. à minuit

5. What time is good for star-gazing?

   A. une heure de l'après-midi (P.M.)

   B. une heure du matin (A.M.)

B **Quelle heure est-il?** *(Use numbers with colons to express each time.)*

> **Modèle:**   Il est huit heures et demie. <u>8:30</u>

1. Il est dix heures moins le quart.   _____

2. Il est trois heures et demie.   _____

3. Il est huit heures.   _____

4. Il est cinq heures dix-sept.   _____

5. Il est une heure.   _____

6. Il est huit heures et quart.   _____

7. Il est midi moins dix.   _____

8. Il est quatre heures vingt.   _____

9. Il est minuit.   _____

10. Il est midi.   _____

Nom: _____   Date: _____

C The 24-Hour Clock. What is it in regular time? For each time on the left, state it in regular time. Add A.M. or P.M.

> **Modèles:** 14h00   2 P.M.
> 21h30   9:30 P.M.

1. 13h00   _____

2. 22h00   _____

3. 17h40   _____

4. 23h51   _____

5. 18h25   _____

D Identify the color generally associated with each item. (*En français, s'il te plaît.*)

1. strawberries   _____

2. rain clouds   _____

3. snowflakes   _____

4. sunflowers   _____

5. crows   _____

6. carrots   _____

7. tree trunks   _____

8. limes   _____

9. lilacs   _____

10. jeans   _____

(Nom): _____   Date: _____

E Color Combinations. Each color on the left is a combination of two others. Do you know what they are? If not, ask your art teacher. Write the colors in French.

1. vert = _____ et _____

2. orange = _____ et _____

3. gris = _____ et _____

4. rose = _____ et _____

5. violet = _____ et _____

F Complete each sentence by choosing the correct word from the box.

> **bleus**   **bleue**   bleu   **bleues**

1. L'océan est _____.

2. La ceinture est _____.

3. Les océans sont _____.

4. Les robes sont _____.

> vert   **verts**   **verte**   vertes

5. La chemise est _____.

6. Le costume est _____.

7. Les chemises sont _____.

8. Les costumes sont _____.

> rouges   rouge

9. La tomate est _____.

10. Les tomates sont _____.

11. Les chemisiers sont _____.

blancs   blanches

12. Les chaussettes sont _____.

13. Les gants sont _____.

G *Mots croisés.* **Complete the following crossword puzzle with vocabulary from this unit.**

Horizontalement

3. after 11:59 P.M.

5. time when the sun is at its highest point in the sky

6. _____ *quelle couleur?*

7. traffic color meaning "go"

9. color of sky on a clear sunny day

10. color of a stop sign

12. color of a carrot

13. _____ *est une heure.*

Verticalement

1. _____ *est-il?* (What time is it?)

2. color of pepper

3. *Il est une heure _____ le quart.* (12:45)

4. late

8. combination of red and white

9. color of salt

11. combination of white and black

H *Parlons!* At what time do you do certain things? Make up a list of ten activities you do on a regular basis. Then find a partner who will choose one activity from your list and ask you at what time you do that activity. You answer in French.

> **Modèle:** A: At what time do you generally eat supper?
> B: à six heures

I *Parlons!* Working in pairs, take turns identifying the colors around you. Your partner must find objects of different colors. He/she says, "I see something in this room that is . . . ." and mentions a color in French. You are to identify that object in French, if you can.

J Review the clippings and answer the questions or give the requested information.

france 2

9.25 KD2A. **11.10** Flash info. **11.20** Les z'amours. **11.55** Championnats d'Europe. Athlétisme. 5e jour. En direct. A Göteborg (Suède). **12.50** Millionnaire.

13.00 JOURNAL

13.50 Hercule Poirot. Film TV. Policier. **15.35** Nestor Burma. Film TV. Policier. **17.10** Championnats d'Europe. Athlétisme. 5e jour. En direct. A Göteborg (Suède).

20.00 JOURNAL

20.50 ★★
Série. Policière.

PJ

Fra. 2004. 3 épisodes. Avec : Bruno Wolkowitch, Thierry Nenez. «Infiltration» (1 et 2/2). Vincent, qui a quitté la PJ, travaille depuis quelques mois pour la BRI. Il tente d'infiltrer une dangereuse équipe de braqueurs de fourgons blindés. - «Enfants de chœur».

Notre avis Opération périlleuse pour Vincent Fournier, obligé d'infiltrer une équipe de braqueurs de fourgons blindés. Trois épisodes rediffusés bien rythmés avec de nombreux rebondissements.

23.45 La boîte à musiques de Jean-François Zygel Magazine. Musical. Invitée: Dee Dee Bridgewater.

0.40 Journal de la nuit. **1.00** A la Maison Blanche. **1.45** Immersion totale. **3.20** Paul-Emile Victor, retour vers le futur. **3.45** 24 heures d'info. **4.06** Dites-le en vidéo. **4.25** Les z'amours. **5.00** 24 heures d'info. **5.30** CD2A.

Demain 20.50 Fort Boyard ★ Divertissement.

1. *À quelle heure commence le film policier* Hercule Poirot?

   _____

2. What kind of movie is it? *(En anglais, s'il te plait.)*

   _____

3. Name the show that comes on at 11:45 P.M.

   _____

4. *Journal de la nuit* begins at 0.40. Express this time in English.

   _____

télé 7 JOURS

Nom: ______________________ Date: ______________________

Transportation times are also given using the 24-hour clock. Answer the questions below about the TGV train that goes from the south of France to Paris. Write the times using the 24-hour clock; then write out the number in French and add the time of day, for example, *14.33* would be expressed as *trois heures moins vingt-sept de l'après-midi.*

HORAIRES

N° du TGV		606	606	666	804	808	814	810	842	820	844
Restauration							(1)				
Nice	D						c	b	7.01	b	10.08
Antibes	D						c	b	7.16	b	10.23
Cannes	D						c	b	7.27	b	10.33
Saint-Raphaël	D						c	b	7.51	b	10.57
Toulon	D				b	b	8.00	b	8.40	b	11.49
Marseille	D				6.42	8.00	8.44	8.47		12.13	
Avignon	D	5.02			7.38	8.55	9.40	9.43		13.07	
Montélimar	D	5.38						10.20		a	
Valence	D	6.00	6.00	6.57		9.48	10.39	10.43		14.01	
Lyon-Part-Dieu	D	7.03	7.03	8.00	9.42						15.06
Le Creusot-TGV	D			8.41							
Paris-Gare de Lyon	A	9.06	9.06	10.10	11.43	12.49	13.39	13.44	13.59	16.59	17.09

5. At what time does train #842 leave Nice?

____

6. When does it arrive in Toulon?

____

7. When does it get into Paris?

____

8. At what time does train #844 leave Cannes?

____

9. At what time does it arrive in Lyon?

____

10. At what time does it get into Paris?

____

Unit 14

A Identify the composer of each work by writing one of these three names:
Jean-Philippe Rameau, Georges Bizet, or Maurice Ravel.

1. *Castor and Pollux* _____

2. *Mother Goose Suite* _____

3. *Symphony in C* _____

4. *Rapsodie espagnole* _____

5. *Carmen* _____

6. *Le Traité d'harmonie* _____

B Match the musical term on the left with its definition on the right.

1. _____ Impressionistic   A. electronic Arabic folk music

2. _____ Baroque   B. modern group influenced by their Basque heritage

3. _____ Romantic   C. stage production for theatrical singers

4. _____ *La valse*   D. 18th-century instrument

5. _____ *le raï*   E. musical style of Rameau

6. _____ *Gipsy Kings*   F. honor for artists and musicians

7. _____ *l'opéra*   G. audio recording of a film

8. _____ sound track   H. musical style of Bizet

9. _____ *Prix de Rome*   I. musical style of Ravel

10. _____ harpsichord   J. ballet by Ravel

C **Circle the letter of the correct answer:**

1. Who started playing music at the age of six?

   A. Rameau   B. Bizet   C. Ravel

2. Who was of Basque ethnic heritage?

   A. Rameau   B. Bizet   C. Ravel

3. Who played the organ?

   A. Rameau   B. Bizet   C. Ravel

4. Who is considered the best Romantic musician and composer from France?

   A. Rameau   B. Bizet   C. Ravel

5. Who has been compared to Vivaldi?

   A. Rameau   B. Bizet   C. Ravel

6. Whose opera was badly criticized when it was first produced?

   A. Rameau   B. Bizet   C. Ravel

7. Whose style is Baroque?

   A. Rameau   B. Bizet   C. Ravel

8. Who wrote music based on nursery rhymes?

   A. Rameau   B. Bizet   C. Ravel

9. Who loved the harpsichord?

   A. Rameau   B. Bizet   C. Ravel

10. Who had a lot in common with Ravel?

    A. Aaron Copland and Manuel de Falla

    B. Wolfgang Amadeus Mozart and Muzio Clementi

    C. Johann Sebastian Bach and Antonio Vivaldi

D **Unscramble the words.**

1. UEMAAR (name) _____

2. ZIETB (name) _____

3. RSICHHDOARP (instrument) _____

4. RUEQABO (musical style) _____

5. TALBEL (type of musical work) _____

E **Match the French name of the musical instrument on the left with its corresponding description on the right. You can easily guess because the French words are cognates!**

1. _____ la clarinette

2. _____ le violon

3. _____ la trompette

4. _____ l'orgue

5. _____ la batterie

6. _____ la flûte

7. _____ la guitare

A. This instrument has pipes, a keyboard, and foot pedals.

B. This instrument is long and straight and often silver.

C. This instrument is beaten with sticks.

D. This instrument is often black.

E. This instrument is played with a bow.

F. This instrument plays reveille, an army wake-up call.

G. This instrument is a favorite of country western and rock singers.

F *Mots croisés.* **Complete the following crossword puzzle with vocabulary from this unit.**

Horizontalement

1. *Pieces for the* _____ (work by Rameau)

7. *La* _____ (work by Ravel)

9. _____ *in C* (work by Bizet)

12. Dion's first name

13. Celtic rap group

14. Baroque composer

Verticalement

2. music that combines Arabic folk music and electronic sounds

3. "The Little _____" (nickname of Edith Piaf)

4. Impressionist composer

5. Romantic composer

6. *Le* _____ *est magicien. (proverbe)*

8. Kidjo's first name

10. Kaas' first name

11. Kidjo's native language

G Interview your speaking partner about his or her musical preferences. Ask the following questions and note the answers. Then reverse roles so that your partner can interview you. Compare and contrast your results.

1. What is your favorite type of music?

   _____

2. What is the name of your favorite group?

   _____

3. Do you (or did you ever) play an instrument? If so, which one(s)?

   _____

4. Do you (or did you ever) join a band or an orchestra?

   _____

5. Do you (or did you ever) participate in a chorus?

   _____

6. Who are your favorite female and male singers?

   _____

7. What is the name of your favorite song?

   _____

8. What do you like better in a song, the melody or the rhythm?

   _____

9. Do you (or did you ever) take dance lessons?

   _____

10. Did you ever do a waltz, rumba, tango, cha cha, foxtrot, swing, polka, or folk dance?

   _____

11. What is the name of a dance that you like?

   _____

12. Who is one of your favorite composers?

   _____

13. What is the name of one of your favorite musical works?

_____

14. Have you ever seen a stage production, such as a musical or an opera?

_____

15. Have you ever gone to a rock concert? Who played?

_____

16. Have you ever been to a classical music concert? Where?

_____

H Review the clippings and answer the questions or provide the requested information.

1. What musical event is happening in the Museum District? (two words, *en français*)

   _____

2. At what time does this event start? (Express this time as P.M.)

   _____

3. *Les marchands,* or shopkeepers, are sponsoring this event. You might remember another word for this occupation. What is it?

   _____

4. In the passage starting with *"Venez,"* find all the words that identify kinds of music.

   _____

5. What does the phrase *soirée de musique* suggest?

   _____

6. Does the phrase in #5 mean the same thing as *soirée musicale?*

   _____

Nom: _____   **Date:** _____

Jeudi 24

ROCK / POP

Jeunesse Apatride, Self Control, Perestroïka, 21h, Café Chaos. **Mountain Radio,** 21h, Main Hall. **Crazydent, N3,** Missy Bar. **Hommage à Ferland: Alex Bay,** 20h, Rendez-vous du Thé. **The Chinese Stars, Foreign Islands,** 21h, Sala Rossa. **Good Time Charlie,** Ye Olde Orchard.

JAZZ / ACTUELLE

Olivier Laroche Duo, Bily Kun. **Shavora,** 19h30, Café des Bois. **The Claremont Standards Band,** 19h30, Clints Grill. **Liza Melfi,** 18h30, House of Jazz. **Michelle Sweeney,** 22h, House of Jazz. **Gadjo Swing,** 18h, Kemia (La). **Opussom,** 21h30, Kemia (La). **DJ Samudaï,** 17h, Quai des Brumes. **Alex Bellegrade, Pierre François,** Upstairs. **Projet Leblanc,** Utopik (L').

FOLK / COUNTRY / BLUES

Stefan McNicoll, 22h, Bistro à Jojo.

HIP-HOP / FUNK

Danny Blanco, DJ Devious, 22h, Boodha Bar. **Pedo Pedro, Gatineau,** Divan Orange (Le). **Martini Funk,** DJ TruSpin. Jello Bar. **The French Connection,** Lola Lounge.

WORLD / REGGAE

Kulcha Connection, 21h30, Bobards (Les). **Orealis,** 21h30, Hurley's. **Raoul,** 23h, Nyk's. **Rapetipetam,** 20h, Théâtre de Verdure. **Pat Greider,** 22h, Vieux Dublin Irish Pub(Le).

ELECTRONICA

Vincent Lemieux, Bily Kun. **Jeudis Adrenaline w/Djs Axel Klein, Omni, X-Cube, Präe,** 22h30, DeLima's. **Dave O'Brien, Deliz,** Kafein. **Overdose w/ DJ Mini,** Parking.

CHANSON

Simplement Streisand, Christine Chartrand. 13h30, Cabaret du Casino. **Roger Genois,** 21h, P'tit Bar. **Mademoiselle S'amuse,** 20h, Théâtre de Verdure.

CLASSIQUE

William C. Maddox, orgue, 12h15, Église St. Andrew & St. Paul.

Name the music category where you will find the:

7. singer Christine Chartrand _____

8. singer Stefan McNicoll _____

9. group Rapetipetam _____

10. organist William C. Maddox _____

11. group *Jeunesse Apatride* _____

12. musician Vincent Lemieux _____

Unit 15

A **Match the French word or expression on the left with its English equivalent on the right.**

1. _____ Il neige.

2. _____ Quel temps fait-il?

3. _____ le printemps

4. _____ froid

5. _____ mal

6. _____ le soleil

7. _____ le vent

8. _____ Quelle est la saison?

9. _____ Il y a des éclairs.

10. _____ Il fait du soleil.

A. sun

B. What's the season?

C. How's the weather?

D. Its snowing.

E. wind

F. bad

G. cold

H. spring

I. The sun is shining.

J. It's/There's lightning.

B **Explain your reasons in French for advising travelers what to pack by writing a logical weather expression.**

1. Take warm clothing.

   En hiver à Lille il fait _____.

2. Take lightweight clothing.

   En été à Marseille il fait _____.

3. Take a coat and a hat.

   En automne à Lyon il fait _____.

4. Take an umbrella.

   Au printemps à Nantes il _____.

5. Take a ski outfit.

   En hiver à St. Moritz il _____.

6. Take a swimsuit.

   En été à Biarritz il fait _____.

7. Take a light jacket.

   Au printemps à Reims il fait _____.

8. Take sunscreen.

   En été en France il fait du _____.

9. Take shorts and T-shirts.

   En été en Europe il fait _____.

C Quelle est la saison? *(Name the season in French when the following weather is typical.)*

1. Il fait beau.   _____

2. Il fait du vent et il pleut.   _____

3. Il neige.   _____

4. Il fait du vent et il fait frais.   _____

5. Il fait humide.   _____

D Name the season in French when the following events usually take place.

1. Many birds fly south.   _____

2. Some animals hibernate.   _____

3. It feels better to be in the shade than in the sun.   _____

4. The air gets warmer and the snow starts to melt.   _____

5. You make jack o'lanterns out of pumpkins.   _____

6. Trees begin to make buds.   _____

E Write a sentence in French that describes the weather associated with each cue.

1. lawn chair

   _____

2. ice skates

   _____

3. lilacs and violets

   _____

4. snowsuit

   _____

5. rake

   _____

6. perspiration

   _____

7. atmospheric electricity

   _____

8. noise in the sky

   _____

9. sunglasses

   _____

10. windmill

   _____

F *Parlons!* Make a list of as many French sentences as you can that describe the weather. Then, working in pairs, say each sentence as a clue for your partner. He or she will say the related season and a related item (clothing or accessory).

> **Modèle:**   A. Il fait du soleil.
> B. l'été; lunettes de soleil

G **Find your way through the seasons. Using the pictures as cues, name the weather conditions you encounter on your way.**

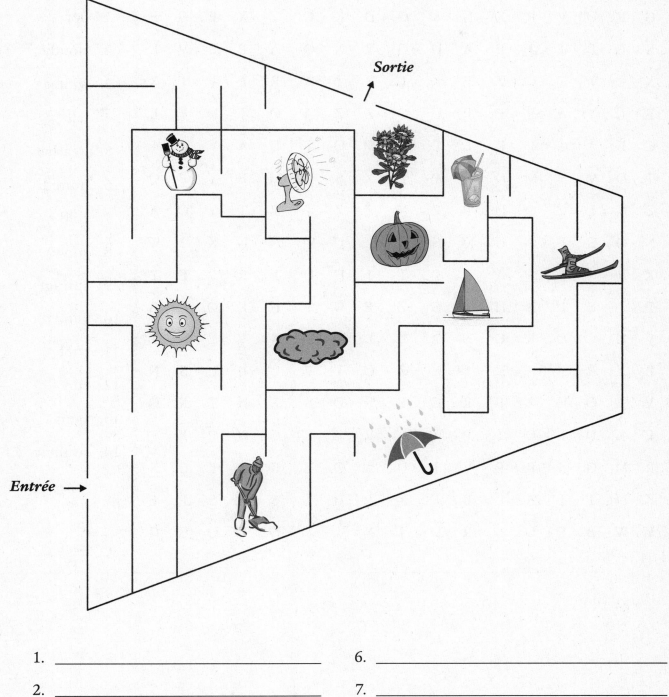

Sortie

Entrée →

1. _____   6. _____

2. _____   7. _____

3. _____   8. _____

4. _____   9. _____

5. _____   10. _____

H *Les lettres cachés.* **Find and circle the French version of the words and expressions listed on the right. Remember that they may go forward, backward, up, down, or diagonally.**

G	F	U	V	R	X	N	S	G	D	K	C	V	X	E	G	F
S	E	P	T	T	E	A	H	G	Y	X	Q	A	P	B	V	L
X	L	W	Z	U	Z	F	K	L	S	I	A	R	F	V	T	X
E	L	Y	A	P	E	P	U	Q	Z	Z	A	O	J	D	Y	L
G	E	J	G	P	R	L	E	N	M	O	T	U	A	V	B	I
I	D	M	Y	M	D	S	P	E	X	S	M	E	T	E	Q
E	N	L	C	Q	D	P	Z	N	Z	Z	J	Z	T	Y	O	A
N	O	S	F	J	U	M	S	U	L	C	W	N	U	K	I	W
K	R	J	W	L	A	E	P	T	I	H	U	P	R	P	F	Z
P	I	S	L	H	H	T	G	Z	E	U	Y	H	K	O	C	B
V	H	C	D	R	C	N	Z	B	L	M	M	W	V	E	N	T
B	Y	R	F	A	N	I	G	Z	O	I	V	U	K	U	S	N
V	E	O	H	Z	F	R	G	F	S	D	S	E	A	T	K	O
P	K	U	L	D	I	P	W	C	R	E	K	G	U	P	X	E
R	M	G	S	R	E	V	I	H	A	O	E	K	Z	L	S	X
K	N	T	I	A	L	B	F	X	L	U	I	S	U	S	P	E
Y	W	B	E	D	L	R	D	J	X	I	F	D	Y	Q	G	G

1. hot
2. cloudy
3. winter
4. fall
5. weather
6. humid
7. cold
8. snow
9. spring
10. wind
11. cool
12. sun
13. rains
14. swallow

I Review the clippings and answer the questions or provide the requested information.

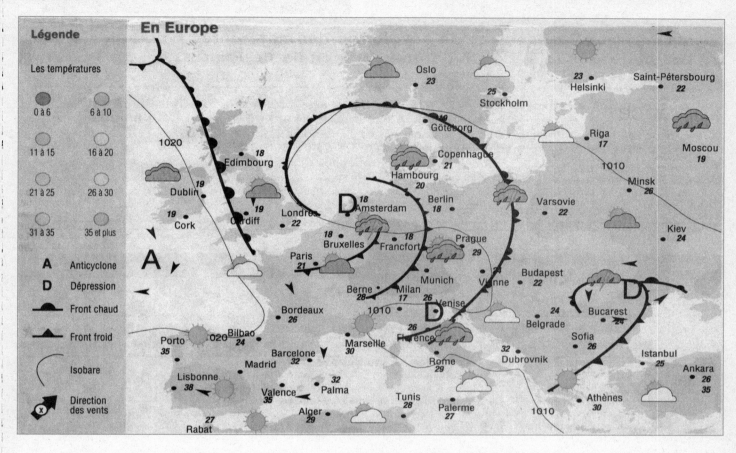

In this section you will be asked to refer to the weather map. First, write a sentence describing the weather in the following cities.

1. Moscou et Dublin

   _____

2. Lisbonne et Athènes

   _____

Next, decide whether the statements below are true *(vrai)* or false *(faux)*.

3. _____ Il y a un front chaud qui va à Londres.

4. _____ Il y a un front froid qui va à Istanbul.

5. What is the purpose of *la météo*?

   _____

6. What is the adjective form of the noun *nuages?*

   _____

7. There is a possibility today of *averses isolées* (isolated showers). How would someone describe this weather?

   _____

8. Three seasons are named. What are they?

   _____

Unit 16

A Match the English words and expressions on the left with the French equivalent on the right.

1. _____ birthday   A. le jour de classe

2. _____ today   B. la semaine

3. _____ week   C. demain

4. _____ day   D. le mois

5. _____ month   E. l'anniversaire

6. _____ school day   F. quand

7. _____ tomorrow   G. hier

8. _____ weekend   H. aujourd'hui

9. _____ yesterday   I. la fin de semaine

10. _____ when   J. le jour

B List the days of the week, starting with the French equivalent for Monday.

> **samedi** *jeudi* **lundi** **dimanche** **mardi** **vendredi** **mercredi**

1. _____

2. _____

3. _____

4. _____

5. _____

6. _____

7. _____

C Complète en français. *(Complete each sentence with the correct day or month in French.)*

1. If today is *mercredi,* tomorrow is _____.

2. If *hier* was Saturday, tomorrow is _____.

3. If this month is *décembre,* next month is _____.

4. If the day before yesterday was *jeudi,* today is _____.

5. If next month is *octobre,* this month is _____.

D Écris en français. *(Write the following dates in French. Follow the model.)*

> **Modèle:** Monday, February 27
> <u>lundi, le 27 février</u>

1. Saturday, June 6 _____

2. Wednesday, October 13 _____

3. Sunday, December 19 _____

4. Friday, May 21 _____

5. Tuesday, August 7 _____

E Écris en français. *(Write in French the day or month as indicated.)*

1. the date when people play jokes on each other _____

2. the month of the U.S. Independence Day _____

3. the month of Valentine cards and chocolate _____

4. the day honoring the Roman goddess of love _____

5. the day honoring the Roman god of war _____

6. the month of Halloween _____

7. the month in which Mother's Day occurs _____

8. the month in which Father's Day occurs _____

9. the day in honor of the moon _____

10. the day in honor of the sun, or "the Lord's day" _____

F Lis les questions. Puis, choisis les réponses correctes. *(Read each question. Then choose the correct answer.)*

1. C'est quand, le jour de fête?

   A. le jour de classe   B. après-demain

2. Quel jour est l'interrogation de français?

   A. mardi   B. semaine

3. C'est quand, la fête des mères?

   A. mai   B. le 31 juillet

4. Qu'est-ce que tu as vendredi?

   A. Je n'ai rien. Je suis libre.   B. C'est le 14 septembre.

5. Qu'est-ce que tu as aujourd'hui?

   A. C'est aujourd'hui jeudi.   B. J'ai une leçon de piano.

6. C'est quand, ton anniversaire?

   A. demain   B. quinze ans

7. Quelle est la date aujourd'hui?

   A. le premier novembre   B. novembre

G With your classmates, play Birthday Lineup in French. In this activity all students will line up in the chronological order of their dates of birth. Begin by asking one classmate his or her birthday.

> **Modèle:**   A: C'est quand, ton anniversaire?
> B: Mon anniversaire est le dix-huit mars.

Then, depending on when **your** birthday is, arrange yourself to the right or left of this person. You will need to ask as many classmates as possible their dates of birth in order to know if you should stand in line to the left or right of them. (Move to the left side of this person if your birthday comes before his or hers; move to the right side of this person if your birthday is after his or hers.) At the end when everyone is lined up in the correct birth order, each of you will say in turn your date of birth. In this way the entire class can check the accuracy of the lineup.

> **Modèle:**
> | Becky | Johnny | Gail | Tim | Joshua |
> |---|---|---|---|---|
> | le 10 mars | le 2 avril | le 29 avril | le 15 mai | le 23 juin |

H **Review clippings and answer questions or provide the requested information.**

AUJOURD'HUI	Ciel variable en matinée, généralement ensoleillé en après-midi. Vents légers. Probabilité de précipitations: 20 %. **Facteur humidex 28.**	**DEMAIN**	Plutôt nuageux avec averses isolées. Probabilité de précipitations: 30 %.
MAXIMUM 25		MAX / MIN 26/13	
CETTE NUIT	Généralement dégagé . Vents légers. Probabilité de précipitations: 0 %. **Facteur humidex 24, en soiree.**	**MERCREDI**	Passages nuageux. Probabilité de précipitations: 10 %.
MINIMUM 17		MAX / MIN 24/13	

When will . . .

1. . . . there be a humidity index of 24?

   _____

2. . . . there be a 10% chance of rain?

   _____

3. . . . it be cloudy with isolated showers?

   _____

4. . . . it be sunny in the afternoon?

   _____

This restaurant, *Tour de Ville*, offers international cuisine during different months of the year. Look closely to find out during which months it offers each kind of food below. (*En français, s'il te plaît.*)

5. Swiss, Austrian, and French

_____

6. Moroccan, Algerian, and Tunisian

_____

7. Italian

_____

8. Japanese and Indonesian

_____

AU RESTAURANT
LES BEAUX JEUDIS

9. Another restaurant is named after a weekday associated with a Roman god. What is the name of this god?

_____

Janvier : Escadron de raies (archipel des Galapagos)   Février : Poisson-clown à collier (Indonésie)   Mars : Récifs coralliens (océan Pacifique)

Every month a certain aquarium provides special exhibits and information about fish and marine life. *(En anglais, s'il te plaît.)*

10. What fish is featured in February?

_____

11. In what month can you learn about sting rays *(raies)*?

_____

12. Many coral reefs are found in the Pacific Ocean. When will there be a special show about them?

_____

Unit 17

A Identify the authors of each work by choosing a name from this list: **Pierre Corneille, Victor Hugo, Charles Baudelaire, Marguerite Duras, or Nathalie Sarraute.**

1. *Les Fleurs du mal* _____

2. *Le Square* _____

3. *Le Planétarium* _____

4. *Les feuilles d'automne* _____

5. *Le Cid* _____

B A literary work may be a novel, a play (comedy or tragedy), a screenplay, a poem (lyric, epic, or dramatic), or an essay, etc. It may also be a collection of poetry or stories. Can you identify the genre of each work below?

1. *Le menteur* _____

2. *Les Misérables* _____

3. *Moderato Cantabile* _____

4. *Les Fleurs du mal* _____

5. *Hiroshima Mon Amour* _____

C Associe les mouvements littéraires avec les noms des auteurs. *(Match the literary movements with the names of the authors.)*

1. _____ Symbolism   A. Hugo

2. _____ the New Novel   B. Sarraute

3. _____ Romanticism   C. Baudelaire

4. _____ Classicism   D. Corneille

D **Write the name of the author that fits each description.**

1. He wrote critical essays on the art of Manet and Delacroix. _____

2. She was originally a lawyer by profession. _____

3. He was originally a lawyer by profession. _____

4. He fought on behalf of the innocent victims of unjust laws. _____

5. She wrote about Vietnam and India. _____

E **Identify the name of the literary work . . .** *(En français, s'il te plaît.)*

1. . . . about a man who steals a loaf of bread.

_____

2. . . . about a woman who is bored with her life.

_____

3. . . . about a man who rings cathedral bells.

_____

4. . . . about the national hero of Spain.

_____

F *C'est à toi!* **What genre (kind) of books do you like to read? Decide if you prefer mysteries, adventure stories, science fiction, or other kinds of stories. Your teacher will designate a corner or another spot in your classroom as a discussion area for a particular genre. Go to the place that represents your favorite kind of reading. Pair up with a partner. Each of you tells the other: 1. why you like these books; 2. the name of the last book of this kind you read; 3. the author; and 4. a brief description of the plot. Then join the other students in your corner and make a list of all your favorite titles. Put this list on the bulletin board and give it a genre title.**

Look at all the lists. What can you say about the reading preferences of the class as a whole? Do your classmates have varied, similar, or surprising tastes?

G *Mots croisés.* Complete the following crossword puzzle with vocabulary from this unit.

Horizontalement

2. worked as a politician for awhile

4. novel by Duras

7. wrote about people in Southeast Asia

8. wrote comedies and tragedies

10. experimented with new kinds of writing

11. what Corneille and Hugo wrote

Verticalement

1. what Duras, Sarraute, and Hugo wrote

3. used picture-words or symbols

5. play by Corneille

6. *Les _____ du mal* (poetry collection by Baudelaire)

9. what Baudelaire and Hugo wrote

H **Review the clippings and answer the questions or provide the requested information.**

Windward Heights
Maryse Condé

Translated from French
by Richard Philcox

Maryse Condé.

1. The well-known author of this novel is from the island of Guadeloupe. Who is she?

   _____

2. Who translated her novel from the original French into English?

   _____

Un homme heureux
Arto Paasilinna
Traduit du finnois par Anne Colin Du Terrail
Éd. Denoël, 256 p., 19 €.

3. Arto Paasilinna is a writer from Finland. What is the French word for the Finnish language?

   _____

4. Who translated his book from the original Finnish into French?

   _____

5. Translate the French title into English.

   _____

6. *Neige* is the title of a novel by Orhan Pamuk, a writer from Turkey. Who translated this book into French?

   _____

7. Translate the title of the book into English.

   _____

8. What is the French word for novel?

   _____

9. What do these words mean in English: *l'écrivain turc?*

   _____

10. Mr. Pamuk was awarded a major prize for world literature. Can you find the name of this prize?

    _____

Orhan Pamuk

Neige
roman
traduit du turc par Jean-François Pérouse

Neige est un extraordinaire roman à suspense qui, tout en jouant habile-ment avec des sujets d'ordre politique très contemporains – comme l'identité de la société turque et la nature du fanatisme religieux –, surprend par ce ton poétique et nostalgique qui, telle la neige, nimbe chaque page.

Le Nobel de littérature décerné à l'écrivain turc Orhan Pamuk

du monde entier
Gallimard

MAGAZINE LITTÉRAIRE N° 446 OCTOBRE 20**

© J. Sassier

La soif de lire

Un roman autobiographique

Écrivains enchanteurs

ROMANS ÉTRANGERS
Stevenson s'embarque
à nouveau dans la Pléiade.

ROMANS FRANÇAIS
Florence Delay et Jacques
Roubaud en quête du Graal.

Find the French words that say:

11. "an autobiographical novel"

_____

12. "the thirst to read"

_____

13. "enchanting writers"

_____

14. "foreign novels"

_____

15. "French novels"

_____

Unit 18

A **Associe les expressions en français avec les expressions en anglais. (Match the French words or expressions on the left with their English equivalents on the right.)**

1. _____ le vélo   A. to dance

2. _____ le match   B. beach

3. _____ faire du cheval   C. to ski

4. _____ la fête   D. bike

5. _____ danser   E. to read

6. _____ la plage   F. museum

7. _____ lire   G. party

8. _____ nager   H. game

9. _____ faire du ski   I. to horseback ride

10. _____ le musée   J. to swim

B Write the sentence from the box underneath the appropriate cue in English.

> Je vais à la boum.   Je vais à la plage.
> Je vais au match.   Je vais au mus e.

1. Balloons, music, and noisemakers

   _____

2. Soccer ball

   _____

3. Paintings, sculptures, and exhibits

   _____

4. Sand bucket, shovel, and seashells

   _____

C Complète chaque phrase. *(Complete each sentence with a word from the box.)*

> soir   adore   pique-nique   veux
> musique   basketball   danser   aussi

1. Je fais du _____.

2. J'aime _____.

3. Il y a demain un _____.

4. Tu _____ m'accompagner?

5. Tu vas à la boum ce _____?

6. Moi _____!

7. Il y a de la _____, n'est-ce pas?

8. J'_____ lire.

D Circle the letter of the best answer to each question.

1. Où vas-tu ce soir?

   A. J'aime nager.

   B. Moi, aussi!

   C. Je vais au match.

2. Où vas-tu aujourd'hui?

   A. Je vais au Festival Delacroix.

   B. Mais oui.

   C. Il fait chaud aujourd'hui.

3. Quels sports fais-tu?

   A. à la plage

   B. du volleyball

   C. pour voir le match

4. Où est le pique-nique?

   A. Il est trois heures.

   B. J'aime nager.

   C. Il est à la plage.

5. Tu veux m'accompagner à la boum?

   A. J'aime faire du ski.

   B. Je fais du football.

   C. Mais oui. J'aime danser.

6. Tu vas à la boum ce soir?

   A. N'est-ce pas?

   B. Bien sûr.

   C. J'aime la musique.

E Unscramble the NOUNS. Add the article before each word.

1. LEGAP   _____

2. NUE-QIEPUQI   _____

3. UBMO   _____

4. LAFOTLOB   _____

5. MEUÉS   _____

6. BELLYLOVAL   _____

7. SUUMEQI   _____

8. THACM   _____

F *Les mots cachés.* **Find and circle the French version of the words and expressions listed on the right. Remember that they may go forward, backward, up, down, or diagonally.**

N	M	C	O	M	M	M	A	N	Z	C	V	C	N	R	W
H	L	W	X	Q	R	Y	G	L	W	T	R	V	J	N	F
G	T	H	Z	Y	L	E	N	N	S	Y	A	R	L	G	O
T	P	D	H	K	W	F	S	O	M	U	S	E	E	E	O
Y	V	N	G	H	N	D	S	N	S	S	P	F	I	L	T
R	Y	A	Z	L	G	Z	O	K	A	Z	M	W	Q	K	B
G	R	G	Q	T	G	C	H	L	F	D	I	T	Q	D	A
J	I	E	L	E	B	V	U	B	E	O	A	S	U	H	L
O	Q	R	S	N	Z	I	M	H	O	V	M	U	W	M	L
Y	D	G	B	N	Q	N	C	R	C	U	R	A	Z	N	V
X	P	V	R	I	S	V	Z	W	E	U	M	P	T	H	F
K	E	N	J	S	X	C	E	E	S	G	Q	U	J	C	H
G	D	E	B	Z	U	M	W	W	Y	G	I	B	V	C	H
D	F	X	R	J	U	C	H	S	T	R	O	P	S	G	J
H	L	F	A	I	R	E	D	U	C	H	E	V	A	L	K
Z	I	Z	B	V	L	G	T	P	L	A	G	E	P	M	S

1. party
2. beach
3. to dance
4. sports
5. to read
6. to go horseback riding
7. museum
8. game
9. soccer
10. tennis
11. to swim
12. bike

G **Quel sport fais-tu?** *(Answer this question according to each set of cues.)*

> **Modèle:** free kick, field goal, pass
> <u>Je fais du football américain</u>.

1. strike, stolen base, inning

   _____

2. spike, serve, net ball

   _____

3. love, deuce, serve

   _____

4. free throw, slam dunk, hoop

   _____

5. goal, cleats, corner kick

   _____

H **Écris en français:**

1. I'm going to the party tonight.

   _____

2. I'm going to the picnic tomorrow.

   _____

3. I'm going to the museum on Saturday.

   _____

4. I'm going to the beach on Sunday.

   _____

I *Parlons!* Interview five of your classmates to find out what they like to do in their free time. Ask each student the questions that follow and write each answer (*Oui* or *Non*) in the space provided. Then summarize your findings.

Camarades de classe:

	Un	Deux	Trois	Quatre	Cinq
1. Est-ce que tu aimes lire?	_____	_____	_____	_____	_____
2. Est-ce que tu aimes danser?	_____	_____	_____	_____	_____
3. Est-ce que tu aimes écrire?	_____	_____	_____	_____	_____
4. Est-ce que tu aimes nager?	_____	_____	_____	_____	_____
5. Est-ce que tu aimes faire du football?	_____	_____	_____	_____	_____
6. Est-ce que tu aimes faire du volleyball?	_____	_____	_____	_____	_____
7. Est-ce que tu aimes faire du cheval?	_____	_____	_____	_____	_____
8. Est-ce que tu aimes faire du vélo?	_____	_____	_____	_____	_____
9. Est-ce que tu aimes parler au téléphone?	_____	_____	_____	_____	_____
10. Est-ce que tu aimes aller *(to go)* au musée?	_____	_____	_____	_____	_____
11. Est-ce que tu aimes aller à la campagne?	_____	_____	_____	_____	_____
12. Est-ce que tu aimes jouer aux jeux vidéos?	_____	_____	_____	_____	_____
13. Est-ce que tu aimes travailler dans le jardin?	_____	_____	_____	_____	_____
14. Est-ce que tu aimes écouter de la musique?	_____	_____	_____	_____	_____

Review the clippings and answer the questions or provide the requested information.

1. The magazine *Côté Sud (South Coast)* includes an ad from a company that wants to build new tennis courts or renovate old ones. Find the two words that express "construction" and "repair."

   _____

2. Underneath the words *Côté Halfcourt* is a slogan. How would you translate it?

   _____

3. What are the dimensions of the *Halfcourt*?

   _____

4. Name the sports that can be played on this court.

   _____

5. Write in French: "I enjoy playing volleyball."

   _____

6. *Il y combien de skieurs?* (Photo A)
    (En français, s'il te plaît.)

    _____

7. *De quelle couleur est la neige? (En français,
    s'il te plaît.)*

    _____

B

8. *Quelle est la saison? (En français, s'il te plaît.)*

    _____

A

9. Write in French: "I like to swim." (Photo B)

    _____

10. Describe photo B by writing in French: "The water is blue."

    _____

11. Tell what season it is in photo B.

    _____

12. How many musical events are listed? *(En français,
    s'il te plaît.)*

    _____

13. On one day every week there is a regularly
    scheduled concert. What day is it? *(En français.)*

    _____

14. Write in French: "I like music."

    _____

15. Write in French: "I'm going to the concert
    tomorrow."

    _____

    _____

PARIS

SELECTION

CONCERTS

ORCHESTRE DES CONCERTS LAMOUREUX
Direction Avi Ostrowsky. Lluis Claret, violoncelle (Wagner, Strauss)
4 février - 17h45
SALLE PLEYEL - 252, faubourg Saint-Honoré - 8e - ✆ (1) 45 63 60 62

LUNDIS MUSICAUX - Jean-Philippe Lafont, baryton
(Haendel, Glück, Mendelssohn, Mozart, Mahler, Schubert, Fauré...)
5 février - 20h30
SALLE GAVEAU - 45, rue La Boétie - 8e - ✆ (1) 49 53 05 07

CONCERTS DU THEATRE GREVIN
Alain Marion, flûte. Danielle Laval, piano (Poulenc, Roussel, Dutilleux)
5 février - 20h30
THEATRE GREVIN - 10, boulevard Montmartre - 9e - ✆ (1) 48 24 16 97

16. What is the date of the concert to be held at the *Théâtre Grevin?*

    _____

Nom: _____   Date: _____

Unit 19

A Circle the item that generally is the most expensive.

1.	une règle	un manteau	trois pêches
2.	un cahier	un verre de lait	un CD
3.	une chaise	cinq tomates	un stylo
4.	un crayon	une chemise	une maison
5.	des baskets	une tasse de chocolat	un mouchoir
6.	une pomme	une chemise	des haricots verts
7.	un ordinateur	un ballon de football	un costume
8.	une tente	une poire	cinquante pêches
9.	une robe	un immeuble	un vélo
10.	deux oranges	un bureau	un pantalon

B Complete each sentence by changing the English word or expression in parentheses to its French equivalent.

1. Je vais acheter des *(some)* _____. *(peaches)*

2. C'est _____, ce CD? *(how much)*

3. Je _____ seulement. *(am looking)*

4. C'est _____. *(all)*

5. Voilà la _____. *(change)*

Exploring French Workbook   **UNIT 19**   **121**

A customer asks about the price of several items. Play the part of the salesclerk as you answer each question. Make up prices in euros that seem reasonable to you.

> **Modèles:** Le chemisier, c'est combien?
> C'est 19,95 euros.
> *or*
> Combien coûte le cahier?
> Ça coûte 1,50 euros.

1. Le blouson, c'est combien?   _____

2. La carte de France, c'est combien?   _____

3. Les biscuits, c'est combien?   _____

4. Combien coûte la pomme?   _____

5. Combien coûtent les haricots verts? _____

D **Circle the letter of the best answer to each question.**

1. Où vas-tu?

   A. Je l'achète.

   B. des baskets

   C. au marché

2. Ce CD, c'est combien?

   A. C'est vingt euros.

   B. Je regarde seulement.

   C. Voilà l'argent.

3. Quelque chose d'autre?

   A. C'est un peu cher.

   B. Voilà la monnaie.

   C. Oui, Madame. Des haricots verts.

4. Est-ce que je peux vous aider?

   A. Je vais au magasin.

   B. Oui. Je voudrais acheter un CD.

   C. C'est un cliente.

5. Qu'est-ce que tu vas acheter?

   A. des chaussures

   B. la caisse

   C. un vendeur

6. Ce pantalon, c'est 25 euros?

   A. Oui, il est en solde.

   B. Voilà l'argent.

   C. Merci beaucoup, Madame.

E **Complète les dialogues.** *(Complete the dialogues.)*

1. A: Est-ce que je peux vous aider?

   B: _____ regarde seulement. Merci.

2. A: Qu'est-ce que tu vas acheter?

   B: _____ baskets.

3. A: Le chocolat, c'est cher?

   B: Non, il est _____.

4. A: _____ vas-tu?

   B: Je vais au centre commercial.

5. A: Quelque chose d'autre?

   B: _____, dix tomates, s'il vous plaît.

F **I. The conversation that follows is between a salesclerk and a customer, but the sentences are all mixed up. Rearrange them by putting them in logical order, beginning with 1 for the first sentence in the dialogue, and 2 for the second, etc. Number 1 is already marked for you.**

___1___ Est-ce que je peux vous aider?

_____ Merci. Quelque chose d'autre?

_____ Oui, Madame. Ce CD, c'est combien?

_____ Bon. Je l'achète. Voilà l'argent.

_____ Ça coûte 14 euros.

_____ Non, c'est tout.

II. Now, in the space below, copy all the sentences in their correct order.

1. _____

2. _____

3. _____

4. _____

5. _____

6. _____

G **Find your way through the store to the cash register. Name the items you encounter on your way.**

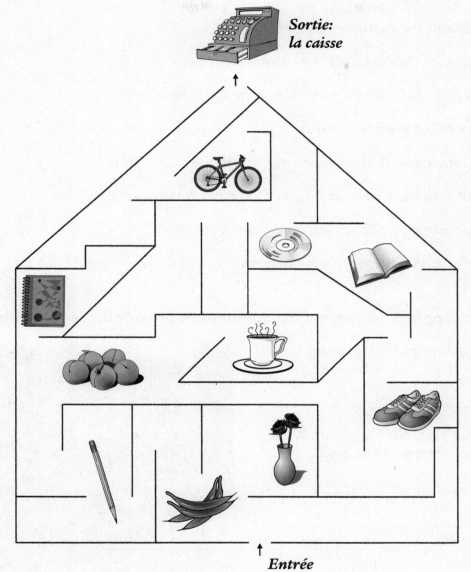

Sortie:
la caisse

Entrée

1. _____

2. _____

3. _____

4. _____

5. _____

6. _____

7. _____

H **Imagine that you are at a shopping center. You and your partner play the roles of a salesclerk and a customer. In the course of the conversation:**

1. The clerk and the customer greet each other.

2. The clerk asks the customer if he wants some help.

3. The customer mentions a particular item and asks its price.

4. The clerk tells the price in euros.

5. The customer says that he or she will buy it.

6. The clerk asks the customer if he or she wants anything else.

7. The customer says, "That's all," and pays for the item.

8. The clerk thanks the customer and gives him or her the change.

I **Review the clippings and answer the questions or provide the requested information.**

1. The French word for "furniture" starts with an "m." What is it?

   _____

   _____

2. This store also sells *objets d'art*. What are some examples of an *objet d'art*?

   _____

   _____

MEUBLES
CONTEMPORAIN
ORIENTAL · ANTIQUE
VIEUX TECK
OBJETS D'ART
CONSEILS EN DESIGN

OSIK DESIGN
www.osik.ca

3. You know the French word for back. Find the expression for "backpack."

   _____

4. This item also comes with a folding seat. Find the words for "folding seat."

   _____

5. *C'est combien, le sac-à-dos?*

   _____

DEUX EN UN Pratique pour les longues marches. *Sac à dos avec siège pliant, 49 €.* Lexon (01.41.10.20.00).

6. When would this particular type of backpack prove useful?

   _____

7. Translate the words *deux en un.*

   _____

8. What kind of store is an *épicerie fine?*

   _____

   _____

Épicerie fine **VANILLE** ÉPICERIE *Gourmet Boutique*

9. Find the word for "small specialty shop."

   _____

10. What is unusual about this watch?

    _____

    _____

11. There are two styles, one at 21 650€ and the other at 22 880€. Each price does not include a comma. What is used instead to separate the thousands from the hundreds?

    _____

12. Would you say that the models of this watch are *bon marché* or *chers?*

    _____

LES HEURES DU MONDE Ici ou ailleurs, à la minute près. *Montre « Heure universelle » en or jaune, 21 650 €, en or blanc, 22 880 €.* Patek Philippe (01.42.44.17.77).

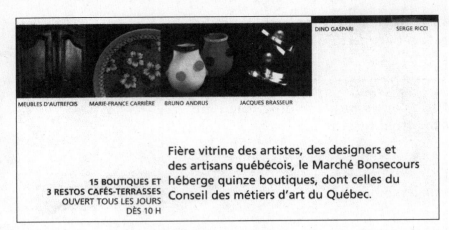

MEUBLES D'AUTREFOIS   MARIE-FRANCE CARRIÈRE   BRUNO ANDRUS   JACQUES BRASSEUR   DINO GASPARI   SERGE RICCI

**15 BOUTIQUES ET
3 RESTOS CAFÉS-TERRASSES
OUVERT TOUS LES JOURS
DÈS 10 H**

Fière vitrine des artistes, des designers et des artisans québécois, le Marché Bonsecours héberge quinze boutiques, dont celles du Conseil des métiers d'art du Québec.

13. Is this place a shopping mall, a store, or a market?

_____

14. *Il y a combien de boutiques (petits magasins) ici?*

_____

EN VENTE CHEZ VOTRE MARCHAND DE JOURNAUX

15. *Journaux* are newspapers. What do you think the sign above means?

_____

Unit 20
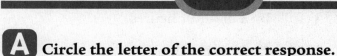

A Circle the letter of the correct response.

1. Who carries a suitcase?

   A. une valise B. une cliente C. une voyageuse

2. What tells you arrival and departure times?

   A. un passeport B. un billet C. un horaire

3. What permits you to travel internationally?

   A. un passeport B. une valise C. une porte

4. How can you get to Clermont-Ferrand?

   A. à midi B. en voiture C. l'employé

5. Which words tell you where something is?

   A. à droite B. à dix-neuf heures C. le prochain train

B Fill in the blanks with a logical word.

1. Le _____ train pour Paris part à quelle heure, Monsieur?

2. Voilà le _____ aller et retour.

3. Descendez à la _____.

4. Pour _____ à l'Hôtel Ritz?

5. L'avion est à la _____ 20.

C **Write the letter of the best answer to each question.**

1. _____ On monte où?

2. _____ Qu'est-ce que tu achètes?

3. _____ Comment s'appelle l'hôtel?

4. _____ À quelle heure part l'autobus?

5. _____ Où sont les vêtements?

A. un billet

B. à dix-huit heures

C. dans la valise

D. à la porte 10

E. le Ritz

D **Give the French name for the vehicle associated with each term. Then, in Part II, write that you travel using each of these vehicles.**

I.

1. l'aéroport _____

2. la gare _____

3. l'océan _____

4. le garage _____

5. le transport en ville _____

II.

> **Modèle:** Je voyage en <u>autobus</u>.

1. _____

2. _____

3. _____

4. _____

5. _____

E Complete each sentence with a word from the box.

> retour avion monte passeports aéroport guichet

1. Je prends le taxi à l' _____.

2. Je prends l'_____ à Paris à treize heures et demie.

3. Je voudrais acheter un billet aller- _____.

4. Je vais acheter un billet au _____ .

5. Où est le contrôle de _____?

6. On _____ où?

F *Parlons!* Imagine that you are in a train station in a French-speaking country. You and your partner play the roles of a clerk at the ticket counter and a traveler. In the course of your conversation:

1. The clerk and the traveler greet each other.

2. The traveler tells the clerk what city he's going to and asks at what time the next train is leaving.

3. The clerk tells the traveler the time.

4. The traveler tells the clerk that he or she would like a round-trip ticket in second class and asks a price.

5. The clerk tells the traveler the price.

6. The traveler pays for the ticket.

7. The clerk thanks the traveler and gives him or her the change.

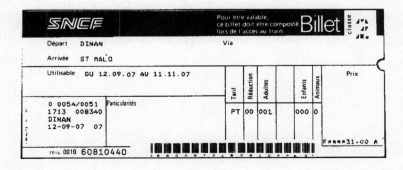

G *Mots croisés.* Complete the following crossword puzzle with vocabulary from this unit.

Horizontalement

4. transportation in the sky
6. place for driving cars
8. departure point at an airport
9. female traveler
11. timetable
12. ticket

Verticalement

1. round-trip
2. transportation on the water
3. place where one finds *les avions*
5. "I travel."
7. document for traveling
9. suitcase
10. train (or bus) station

H **Review the clippings and answer the questions or provide the requested information.**

1. What tells you that bus #63 serves the city of Paris?

   _____

2. Write the number above in French.

   _____

3. What are the two end points of the bus route?

   _____

   _____

4. What is the profession of the man in the foreground?

   _____

5. Write the abbreviation for *Sociéte Nationale de Chemin de Fer.*

   _____

6. When does this message suggest that you travel by train?

   _____

7. Write in French: "I like to travel."

   _____

8. What can one rent at this agency? *(En français, s'il te plaît.)*

_____

9. The vehicles are described as *économiques*. Does that word suggest they are *chers* or *bon marché*?

_____

10. The ad suggests that if you rent from this agency, you will drive an environmentally friendly vehicle. What word, do you think, presents this idea?

_____

roulez *écolo*

AUTOPLATEAU
LOCATION DE VOITURES ÉCONOMIQUES

CAR RENTAL · ALQUILER DE AUTOS · ALUGUEL DE CARROS

3585, Berri suite 110 * (514) 281.5000 * 🚇Sherbrooke
Centre Infotouriste, 1001 Square Dorchester * 🚇Peel
www.autoplateau.com * 1-877-281-5001

GARE AEROPORT CHARLES-DE-GAULLE TGV :
PASSEZ DIRECTEMENT DU TGV A L'AVION.

TGV *Prenez le temps d'aller vite.*

166
BD PN   872737874968
08704533310202

:DV 273787496
:CC900000920   PARIS LYON B   310700   10H39
:897990   Dossier QPYQQM   Page 1/1

11. *Comment s'appelle l'aéroport?*

_____

12. *TGV* means a high speed train. What does this ticket allow you to do?

_____